Something In The Water

& Other Tales Of Homeopathy

Something In The Water

& Other Tales Of Homeopathy

Sue Lanzon

2012

ISBN 9781-874581-802 r0

Cover design by Sue Lanzon & Colin Winter
Cover image 'Storm at Sea' by Michael Eldridge,
www.michaeleldridge.net

Grateful acknowledgement is made to the following for their kind permission to quote copyright material: Random House Inc (Schocken Books) for the quotation from The Periodic Table by Primo Levi; Faber & Faber for quotations from Waiting For Godot by Samuel Beckett and for the quotation from The Waste Land by T.S. Eliot; Rudolf Steiner Press (Sophia Books) for the quotation from Medicine, Mythology and Spirituality by Ralph Twentyman; Ninth House Publishing for the quotation from Portraits of Homeopathic Medicine: Vol.1 by Catherine R. Coulter; David Higham Associates for the quotation from The End Of The Affair by Graham Greene (Vintage); Granta Books for the quotation from Straw Dogs by John Gray; The Bertrand Russell Peace Foundation.

Printed by Berforts Information Press Ltd, Stevenage, UK

Published by Winter Press in 2012

Winter Press
16 Stambourne Way
West Wickham, Kent BR4 9NF
e: sitw@winterpress.net

For my children

'...That if one looked for the bridge, the missing link, between the world of words and the world of things, one did not have to look far.'

Primo Levi -The Periodic Table

Author's Note

E. L. Doctorow once said:

'I am led to the proposition that there is no fiction or nonfiction as we commonly understand the distinction; there is only narrative.'

It is in the spirit of that proposition that I have constructed these stories – to protect patient confidentiality and to spare the blushes of my friends.

Some characters are based on real people, some are entirely fictitious, some are an amalgamation. Some real people appear in more than one disguise.

Similarly, events depicted here are a combination of the real and the possible.

Contents

Acknowledgements

In the writing of this book, I am indebted to the following:

Fabian Acker, Geoff Baker, Nick Chow, George Jisho Robertson and Alison Winfield-Chislett, for reading anything I put in front of them, for being generous with their time and firm, yet merciful, with their critiques; The East Dulwich Writers' Group, for dealing me in at the writers' table, encouraging me to show my hand and provoking me into upping my game; Sandra Goodman of Positive Health magazine, for publishing earlier versions of the first few chapters, and being the first person to appreciate what I was trying to do; Colin Winter of Winter Press, for his patience, enthusiasm and attention to detail; Martin Walker, for contributing the Foreword, despite juggling several other projects, and for his tireless campaigning on behalf of complementary medicine; David Colquhoun, Edzard Ernst, Ben Goldacre, Sense about Science et al, without whose tireless campaigning against homeopathy I might never have felt the need to try and demystify it to a wider world; Les Hall, for the joke.

Foreword

by Martin J. Walker

Something in the Water is a book about homeopathy, its practice and its remedies. It is, however, not an ordinary book but a rare one, which echoes the story of its subject in both form and content. The broken narrative of incidental tales, recounted in the first person by a practicing homeopath – someone who thinks homeopathically – offers us an everyday understanding of the homeopath and of homeopathy. The education we are offered, however, is not from a factual, pragmatic or linear viewpoint, but immerses the reader in the very idea of its process. Imagine, if you can, being an English speaker opening a book about the Turkish language and finding part of the narrative itself written in understandable Turkish.

The book describes, in entertaining terms, the holism of homeopathy. This holism, not the mechanics of the practice or the effect of the remedies, is what sets homeopathy apart from 'scientific' or allopathic medicine. Homeopathy, as this book tells us, stretches like a live wire between the practitioner and her environment, the patient and her environment, the relationship between practitioner and patient and the onward journey in the life of both these parties. The idea behind *Something In The Water* is post-modern.

Each chapter of the book is a short story, mined from the homeopath's life, in which a prominent character exhibits the need for a remedy or a situation recalls some aspect of homeopathic practice. The first story, entitled *The Liver*, introduces the major themes of the book; we are, for the most part, in the inner city; homeopathy is rooted in the everyday; the author is writing from a political, undogmatic perspective; the homeopath's private and professional lives continually merge with and mirror each other.

The other tales range across many aspects of human activity, identity and geography. Some drag you in without resistance while others force you to do your own deductive reasoning. Some seem to have more complex messages than others. For example, *The Homeopath Is Not In* connects domestic problems with the terror of South American politics in the 1980s, while describing the remedies, Stannum and Silica. In the title story, *Something In The Water,* ancient Greek mythology, family concerns, gender stereotypes, romance and the remedy Sepia find a connection on an Aegean island. In all, there are 21 stories, including the wonderfully titled *Shut Up And Talk*.

The idea of postmodernism means that subjects can be addressed by referring to matters apparently unrelated to the narrative's core phenomena. An earlier 'modernist' book about homeopathy would probably discuss its history, its reputed mechanisms and its use following diagnosis. The lengthiest part of the book may have been given over to a complex diagnostic analysis. The modern way of describing homeopathy or anything else was mainly linear and logical.

Of course, there is nothing wrong with this. However, homeopathy, despite its age, is, in its diagnostic method and treatment fundamentals, profoundly post-modern; that is to say it appears anything but linear and logical and is even, in part, unknown. A simple analogy could be found in a comparison between the modern fictitious Scotland Yard detective and Sherlock Holmes. The modern Scotland Yard detective is always separated from his community as a professional worker; he solves cases by moving under orders, pragmatically from one material clue to the next. If he finds no clues, the most fundamental question of whether or not a crime even exists will be raised. Sherlock Holmes, on the other hand, especially rendered by the late Jeremy Brett[1], the acknowledged master of the identity, acts as an independent, perverse and unaccountable 'private' detective, personally challenged by drug taking and depression, creating his own clues. Holmes solves cases by drawing upon intuitive wisdom, experience of life, emotional catharsis, acute observation of a variety of signs, observation of the demeanour of witnesses – contextualising environmental clues, long gathered tangential notes, news clippings and a febrile imagination, all of which dynamically link apparently unconnected phenomena and described cause and effect. While it might be suggested that the modern fictional detective is rational and scientific and Holmes irrational and entirely intuitive, in fact Holmes's intellect would have welcomed the detailed pictures provided by post-modern forensic science.

Since the advent of the 'modern' and corporate scientific period, life has come to be described with a reductionist facility. We have become increasingly used to acting as if life between birth and death was as simply understood and as automatic as drowning when the lungs fill with water. But human identity and the human condition are complex formulations often needing, in the field of medical diagnosis and treatment, individual solutions. While modern allopathic medicine responds only to a snap shot, the end point of linear explanation, at one place with an immediate

1 Sherlock Holmes, The Complete Collection. 1984-1988, 1991-1994. A Granada Television Production. ITV.

and practical understanding of the present, homeopathic diagnosis traverses a grid which stretches back into the past and forward into the future, from the mental to the material, from the un-manifest to the observed.

Signs of the idiosyncratic nature of the human identity are all around us but the environmental context, the history, the individuality, the mind and the interlinking relationships which form the human identity, confound or are ignored by allopathic medical practitioners. The fathers of allopathic medicine were competent mechanics, men who learnt most from butchering live animals and cutting up already dead humans. The idea that there might be a nexus between a failing part of the body's structure and either the personality or the surrounding environment was alien to the majority of them and, to their heirs, still is. Anyone who introduces complexity into the medical paradigm, who thinks of introducing environmental static into diagnosis, is ridiculed, berated and sent into intellectual exile. This conflict over differences in methodology when studying cause and effect crops up in other areas. In the science of epidemiology, for instance, this same division between diagnostic simplicity of cause and effect and the more complex nature of holistic analysis of cause can occur.

In Oxford in the 1960s, the brilliant epidemiologist Alice Stewart[2] found herself in an undeclared academic conflict with Sir Richard Doll, a man groomed by the British state and corporate interests to be the world's most renowned epidemiologist. Both teaching and researching at Oxford, the two scientists represented extreme poles of research

2 Gayle Greene (1999) The Woman Who Knew Too Much: Alice Stewart and the Secrets of Radiation, University of Michigan Press.

methods and the strategic use of their results. While Stewart's work on the prevalence of cancer was carried out on behalf of the people for whom she was happy to give evidence in claimants' cases, Doll worked only for corporate interests, giving evidence in their defence.[3]

The main difference in the life of these two scientists involved their widely different methodologies. Doll once suggested that if causal factors could not be proven quickly in a well-structured research project they were probably not worth proving. He argued this simplistic approach to causation as a hedge against the emergence of more hidden and subtle effects of corporate toxins such as pesticides that were beginning to emerge in the second half of the 20th century. Stewart, on the other hand, spent her life working on projects for which she never stopped gathering evidence. Stewart's brilliant insistence that all data was relevant and the scientist must listen to the 'background noise', the static of random data that surrounds subjects, could be the motto of any homeopath. Homeopathy is deeply concerned with 'background noise' – psychological, intuitive, environmental and emotionally obscured evidence.

It is only very recently that the consideration of ill health, as separate from the structure of the efficient human body, has been labelled as science and nothing but science. Everyone but believers in allopathy (and even some of them are confused) knows that understanding health care, diagnosis and treatment as science was from the beginning a most

3 This scientist, most often cited as the man who discovered the link between smoking and cancer, towards the end of his life was presented to give expert evidence on behalf of corporations for the lawyers, Covington and Burling, the legal firm that laid the foundations for the defence of tobacco against claims that it caused cancer.

terrible mistake – the point at which the charabanc full of the weekly soap's characters leaves the road to plunge down the ravine. The study and correction of human ill health is not a science. Science, inevitably, is based upon material certainties, whereas the treatment of ill health and idiosyncratic lack of wellness entails in many cases a wide-ranging, speculative and intuitive process of detection.

It is part of the platform of the present attack by corporatists on homeopathy that it would not be preferred as a treatment following a car crash. Of course, this is a straw man – even worse, a straw man of no stature that doesn't need knocking down. No homeopath would ever suggest that homeopathy could resurrect a badly damaged human body after a car accident. There is nothing in *Something in the Water* that describes homeopathic treatments following car accidents, rather it reflects upon subtle conditions within almost normative social circumstances where homeopathy is, undoubtedly, useful and effective.

Such circumstances would of course include helping the body heal and recover more efficiently from a car accident, helping deal with shock or bereavement after an accident and toning down the fears of the badly injured patient. All of these later conditions the allopaths ignore as they trundle the broken human machine from corridor gurney to operating theatre, to bed and quickly back onto the street.

So who will profit most from this well-crafted and involving book? Homeopathic practitioners will, no doubt, read it with an eye to its technical correctness; some who don't completely understand their own craft could well learn the lessons of the remedies cited. Above and beyond this, it is an ideal book for any reader new to homeopathy – for it explains this great method of healing, and what might be expected from its uses, in the simplest and most readable form. Consequently it could prompt many individuals to find their way to the therapy.

With homeopathy presently under concerted attack from lobby groups and corporate scientists, it needs defenders, proselytizers and prophets. Like other professionals who have become embattled in the war for science and new technology, some leading homeopaths think that their salvation lies in an exacting scientific explanation of their craft. I personally don't believe that this is a path to be taken with any urgency or at the exclusion of other more popular routes. In time the science of homeopathy will be discovered. In fact this process has already begun.[4]

Exacting explanations by science won't right the slant of the playing field or lead to its levelling, nor will it remedy the worldly ignorance of skeptics and corporate scientists. Real change will only occur when the hearts and minds, the lives of individuals and communities, are changed by discussions about the advantages of homeopathy over pharmaceutical medicine and a more positive education and understanding of homeopathy in the community. Sue Lanzon's book is one of the first to embark upon this promotion and the first to do this using a common, popular language of the people.

Martin J Walker.

4 Luc Montagnier's latest work, which he says shows that water retains the imprint of substances even in minute doses, building on that of Jacques Benveniste's in 1988. Benveniste et al, Nature (vol 333, p 816) 1988.

The Liver

Here she comes, her black robe billowing, her children trailing in her wake. She shouts at the little one to say hello to me, then tells him off for interrupting. They're Bengali. They have problems with the downstairs neighbours who call them, inaccurately and with great malice, Paki bastards. This happens for the most part at random, but always occurs during festivals and other special days when they dare to entertain at home. When they are, relatively speaking, having a good time. One of the many shortcomings of cheaply built public housing is the lack of sound-proofing. Not only do the walls have ears, but the floors and ceilings as well. This determines more than the material quality of shelter. It condemns her family to a recurring mathematical formula. Celebratory rites, and the right to celebrate, equals another load of racial abuse.

The children were all on asthma medication when I started seeing them. She'd lost count of the number of antibiotics they'd had. I've been directing treatment towards clearing their lungs and cleansing their blood – unsupressing, if there is such a word. They're doing well, but there's so many of them and they cough a lot.

My actress daughter, Tina, had phoned five minutes before to tell me the great news. She'd got the part.

"Guess what, Mum. I'm playing a slut again."

"Fantastic, darling," I say, encouragingly, whilst wondering what thirty years of feminism has really taught me. I also wonder what this devout Muslim woman would make of it if she knew. I experience, not for the first time, a split between my private self and my homeopath persona. I shake it off and pay attention to what she is saying.

The police were called but did nothing, as usual. Her eldest son had to be restrained. Everyone was upset and the evening, yet another evening, ruined.

She pulls up her robe and assorted jumpers and shows me where it hurts. Right side, behind the ribs – the liver. She's been scanned, palpated and the medics can find nothing wrong. They've diagnosed stress, and she's been given anti-depressants. She hasn't taken them. But her digestive system isn't working properly and her liver, well, it hurts. What am I able to do for her, she asks. What should she take?

I have been trained to view the body in relation to the mind and the emotions. That's common to all holistic traditions and I borrow heavily from various maps, aligning the European road-trip that is homeopathy with, among others, the Chinese medical system. This is an ancient pathway and can be consulted as a kind of Rough Guide to the Organs.

The topography goes like this: when we withdraw our awareness from our emotional pain, the emotion lodges in an organ and the body reacts. The liver is where we store our anger, and our anxiety concerning the past or future. The Liver is 'One Who Lives.'

If there is an inability or unwillingness to be engaged with the here and now but rather to dwell in the failed past or project an unsafe future, the liver becomes compromised. If we suppress our anger, or express it too much, the liver becomes irritated. This does not show up on a scan.

"Well," I say, "you could try and stop shouting at the kids."

"Yes, I know," she says, "but if they make a noise the downstairs neighbours start banging on the ceiling, isn't it. Then, sometimes, four in the morning they do it, just to stop us sleeping. I shouting at children to keep them quiet."

Four in the morning. Liver time. At 4 a.m. the liver is at its most active, at the height of its assimilative process.

How neat, I think, as she riffles through a plastic bag and pulls out a crumpled packet of tablets.

"Those last pills you give me. I think they helped a bit."

"Good." I reply, unclear as to whether this is true or something that we both wish to be true.

"What else can you do for me?" she asks again, "What should I take?"

I am always touched by her reverence for homeopathy, which comes from a life-time of familiarity. Back home, her mother always used my kind of medicine for the family. She will not take anything, not even a vitamin, without consulting me first. I feel she looks upon me as some kind of benign, light-skinned avatar, a link with her home and her ancestral knowledge, though I've never been to Bangladesh and we meet in a crummy portakabin in London. She trusts in me because I am her doctor. Which, of course, I'm not.

Homeopathy, as we who practice it are so fond of telling you, can be used to treat more than just coughs, colds and nappy rash. It's powerful stuff.

The anger of the downstairs neighbours makes me feel defeated and ashamed of my race. The anger of the woman in front of me, chin resting on her clenched fists as she waits for me to come up with the solution to the torturous puzzle of her family's health-care, is spilling out in all the wrong places. I try and gather it up for her to look at, but I know I'm only chasing ghosts.

I prescribe a liver tonic and something for each of the children. I book their next appointment for a few weeks time. I expect she'll phone me in a couple of days because one of them will be coughing too much at night, loud enough to wake the neighbours. Step by step, we make our way together – it's a slow process.[1]

1 If you skipped the Foreword, now's the time to read p. xiii/xiv – Ed

The Poison Nut

Sunday afternoon, the bar is crowded. I'm waiting for a friend. Perched on a stool, sipping my Earl Grey, I feel quietly superior to the drunken punters who surround me. Bright young things with money to burn and the world at their feet. Is it the tea causing me to think in clichés, or am I just tired?

A familiar face emerges from the Gents. Someone I know vaguely from my clubbing days. He's celebrating, just won a big contract. Swaying slightly, he beckons to someone else over my shoulder.

"That's my brother." he says proudly, as I turn around. A man lurches towards us. Handsome, wearing an expensive suit, he's looking at me like I'm lunch or possibly, by this time, dessert. I can tell he's having trouble focusing.

"Hi," he says, thrusting his face and body into the area I regard as my defensible space, "I'm Tiny. Pissed Off P.R."

I smell alcohol, tobacco, something spicy.

"What you drinking, babe?" He gestures aggressively to the barman. "Oi, Cicero! We'll have another round of Bellinis, pronto, my man and... a cup of tea? Hang on, I could do with an espresso myself, yeah, cool babe. Coffee, it's my saviour, know what I mean? Homeopathy? What's that, massage and stuff? Have you thought about expanding your client-base? Here's my card. Maybe we should get together, crucial, y'know. Shit, I'm vibrating!"

He takes his mobile phone out of his back pocket, reads a text, grins at me.

"My broker," he explains.

In the meantime, his brother has disappeared after a woman in a particularly short skirt and spiky boots. I'm trapped.

Tiny? I wonder. Does that denote penile insufficency, brain capacity, an excess of confidence or what? By now he's holding a drink in each hand, two phones and an unlit cigarette.

"Don't tell me," I say, "you've got a red car, double-parked."

"Right outside, babe. It's ready to go, just like me. You wanna come for a ride?"

He looks deep into my eyes and adjusts his crotch.

"And you're having trouble with your... insides."

"How did...?"

"Your stomach is inflamed. You have terrible indigestion."

"Wicked!"

"An ulcer?"

"Top ranking, babe. What was it you said you did? Astrology?"

As Tiny leans his body further towards mine in a blatantly sexual but somehow absent way, a man carrying a tray of drinks accidentally knocks his elbow. Tiny whirls round, the end of his cigarette just missing the eye of a passing waiter. He is deeply affronted.

"Sorry, mate," the man says.

"You will be," Tiny snarls, "... fucking moron." He turns back to me, baring his teeth.

The friend I've been waiting for materialises at my side, shaking raindrops from his glistening black hair.

"Sorry I'm late." He gives me a hug. Tiny laughs.

Remi is a biochemist from Pakistan. Lithe, relaxed, beautiful, he emanates a watery presence which flows over me, dampening the onslaught of Tiny's fire and allowing me to relax a little too. He can tell what needs doing straight away.

"Look, there's a table." He points to the far side of the bar where two women are getting ready to leave. "Nice meeting you."

"Later, man," Tiny drools. "Know what I mean?"

Nux Vomica, the poison nut, literally 'the nut which makes you vomit', is a remedy which has been encountered by many who are not regular users of homeopathy. This is because it is a fantastic cure for hangovers.

It can also be spotted, energetically speaking, all over the inner and outer city. Wherever there is noise, bustle, commerce, competition, deadlines, targets or traffic jams, Nux Vomica will be present. Think road rage. It is indeed a driven state. There is an irritation of the nervous system which can produce, or be caused by, a craving for stimulants. There is hurriedness and impatience, a feeling that time passes too slowly, which can lead to explosive anger. The mind is over-active and excitable. There is egotism and a tendency to blame others, overt sexuality and performance anxiety. The functional disturbances and pathology caused by the poison, and healed by the remedy, centre mainly around the digestive system. The heat of all this burning impatience and desire inflames, corrodes and ulcerates. Tiny's prescription was easy.

"So why don't you give him some?" Remi asks. "I bet you've got a bottle in that little bag of yours, haven't you?

Just for emergencies." He nudges me, winking, "Know what I mean?"

"It's my day off!" I snap. Hell, this Nux Vomica energy is catching. "Anyway, he hasn't asked me. You know I gave up proselytising years ago."

"You could slip it into his pink fizz. Spike his drink with its very antidote. From a biochemical point of view..."

"Don't bring science into this, please."

"Why not? Knowing how to deal with the toxins in your life is a vital step towards self-realization." He takes my hand and traces the lines of my palm.

"You're just being patronising," I mutter, retrieving my hand which has begun to sweat." A person's got to want to heal."

"Yes," he says, "but sometimes we don't know what we want until someone points it out to us, do we?"

"I think Tiny likes being Tiny. Look at him."

By this time, the man in question has wrapped himself around a leggy blonde, leering into her cleavage and drumming his fingers on the base of her spine. She's teetering on the edge of a bar-stool, tossing her golden mane and running her scarlet nails down the inside of his thigh. The clichés fill up the space inside my empty cup.

"Now you're being patronising," Remi says.

"Nonsense!" I retort. "We're all nuts full of poison in one way or another. Besides, I happen to understand addiction. Oi, Cicero! Another cuppa, pronto!"

Looking For Clues

'Since I discovered the unconscious, I find myself much more interesting.'

Sigmund Freud

He sits opposite me. He's asked to be there, in my consulting room. He's paying for my time. Yet his legs are crossed, his arms are folded, his body slants away from me at a curiously uncomfortable-looking angle as if he's trying to make a break for the door with his shoulder.

'Why is he shielding his left side?' I wonder, shifting my own body to mirror his position.

She tells me something completely, horrifically, spine-chillingly awful about her personal life and bursts out laughing. Has she noticed I'm not laughing with her? Should I mention it? Her grimace reminds me of a chimpanzee in distress.

Instead of saying "My children are driving me nuts" he says "My children are driving *you* nuts." Is he referring to himself here as one of my children? Does he really want to say *I'm* driving *him* nuts? Would Sigmund find this funny?

Then there's the one who, in telling me her current problem, perfectly reflects some aspect of my own. She starts to talk and I know what she's going to say next because I woke up dealing with the same thing and… she says it. I'm aware of struggling not to betray myself. It's a close call. She sees a flicker of my eyelids and some part of her recognizes I am in a state of empathy, of rapport, beyond the usual. She doesn't know she knows this. I concentrate very carefully as I suspect she has something unspoken about her person which I need to recognize in some way. As I offer her a new perspective on her situation, which may help her to deal with it more effectively, I realize that I'm telling myself what to do.

Erroll, my next-door neighbour and a tough cookie, says to me, "Have you ever thought about the fact that if you put a space between the 'e' and the 'r' of the word 'therapist', it looks like 'the rapist'?"

His wife, Marjorie, a goddess whose wisdom and beauty are renowned throughout South London and beyond, sneers knowingly at the dark circles under my eyes.

"Your adrenals are shot, darlin'. Too much time spent listenin' to other people's crap. It's too excitin' for yer."

"So which is it?" I bleat, glancing down at the cup of dark, bitter liquid Marjorie has thrust into my hand. "Certainly, it can be argued that the uneven power dynamic between therapist and patient will inevitably render the patient a victim on some level. However, as any homeopath will tell you, the existence of psychic vampires masquerading as unwell humans is an undisputed reality."

"Just be quiet now and drink." Marjorie says.

Later, whilst lying in a very hot bath wondering if my adrenals are enjoying the rest or being pushed further into meltdown by the temperature of the water, my thoughts return to the opposing forces that can infect a therapeutic relationship, and the constructs that shape its direction.

Since I discovered the unconscious, I find myself to be much more aware of the delicacy of human communication. I endeavour to translate a language whose meaning is unknown whilst being *constantly* reminded, (I'd just like to take a moment here to thank all my teachers, patients, children, parents, lovers, friends, cats and my many, many fans who've made it possible for me to be lying in this bath today, being reminded), that my translation is, by its nature, a subjective one. The only way I can ensure that my skill as a healer is not corrupted by this is to anticipate synergy – the making of something greater than the sum of its parts.

I need to meet the patient as an equal in our humanity; provide a safe space between us in which they can lay out the concerns that have driven them to come; note all the different nuances of communication happening simultaneously on the physical, mental, emotional and spiritual levels; put them into some kind of coherent pattern or shape; scan my conclusions for contamination from my own issues; scan myself for vampire bites; offer this new configuration back in a way that invites the patient to participate in their own healing, and gives them something constructive to take home; accept resistance or denial as useful information regarding the pace of change; reflect on what the patient in turn has given me in the way of new insight and knowledge and somewhere, in among all this, prescribe a remedy.

(You may wonder why it is that homeopaths always have to look things up in books. Well, guess what, we're not looking anything up at all. We're just playing for time. You think you've come for a little something for your eczema? Think again).

Hopefully, this dynamic interchange between us acts as a conduit for mutual growth. The tricky bit lies in receiving the unconscious messages whilst not getting caught up in my own interpretation. No wonder we call it practicing.

The bathwater is now the wrong side of tepid. I reach for a towel, hoping I've succeeded in forestalling burnout for another day. Burnout? Meltdown? All this heat-inspired imagery. Is my unconscious trying to tell me something? Has the bath scorched my linguistic faculties? What was in that drink Marjorie gave me, anyway? Why do I ask so many questions?

The phone rings. It's Erroll to say my cat's been pooing on his lawn again.

"How do you know it's not foxes?" I counter, paradoxically now sharp as a pin after my long soak.

"Because," he says, "I happen to know cat shit when I see it."

A long line of question marks skid to a halt as I confront Erroll's grasp of certainty, so much more muscular than my own. Then, realizing he's waiting for a reply and noticing I'm dripping bathwater into the receiver, I yawn.

"Can we investigate tomorrow in the daylight, please, Erroll? Things will be a lot clearer then," I say, rather pleased at my own impromptu stab at being sure of something, even if all I'm sure of is that things are unclear right now.

"Why not?" he says. "Come by for a Marjorie Special in the morning."

I look at my indistinct reflection in the mirror. Somebody once said that those who have all the answers are probably asking the wrong questions. As I rehearse giving this news to Erroll, the foxes start their nightly mating ritual – a noise which has become part of our inner city lives and which makes me think more of pigs being slaughtered than foxes obeying a biological imperative – then I think again. Instead I'll tell him that the word 'therapist' comes from the Greek *theraps*, one who escorted the coffin at a funeral and can be translated therefore as one who travels alongside or, stretching the allusion further, a neighbour.

The clues are not in the sound of things, nor how they look nor even how they feel. It's the spaces between the objects that make synergy possible.

No doubt he'll think of something coruscating in reply, which will make me laugh as, together, we check the evidence on the lawn.

The Life Of The Mind

Courtauld Institute, The Strand. My friend, Jessie, has dragged me here for a lecture on D.H. Lawrence, given by a writer she greatly admires. She admired his last book so much that she decided, on turning the last page, she wanted to marry him.

"I feel I need a writer in my life," she says.

"Why?"

"Because..." She pauses outside the Courtauld entrance and looks skyward as the first few flakes of snow arrive with us at the threshold leading to the Royal Sociey Of Literature, "... because I want to be written."

Inside, I play Spot The Critical Theorist as the lecture hall fills. I notice I've already started thinking in Upper Case.

"I don't, in fact, know the first thing about D. H. Lawrence..." Jessie says, suddenly peering into the abyss of her own ignorance.

"I don't either..." I lie, as The Writer arrives – a tall, skinny, dishevelled aesthete with a large red nose, and a chaotic sheaf of notes, he clears his throat and furrows his extremely high and pimply brow "... but your husband-to-be probably knows enough for all of us."

"Sshh," a woman behind me hisses intellectually as The Writer begins.

The man sitting on my right has an odour redolent of decades of literary struggle in un-aired, dusty rooms. My chair is uncomfortable. I have a great view of the back of someone's head and amuse myself for a few nanoseconds by diagnosing her current health problems from the texture of the skin on her neck and the position of her right shoulder. It's a thing we complementary therapists do in idle moments when there are no copies of the Times Literary Supplement to peruse. It's called Reading The Body.

The Writer is droning on in a vainglorious, bombastic sort of way about the demise of the Novel of Ideas. I find myself anticipating my snowbound journey home courtesy of South East Trains, and decide I'd better have a couple of glasses of publisher's plonk before setting off. Everyone else appears to be riveted. The air is rapt with Reverence for the Intellect. The Writer mentions loins at one point and my ears prick up momentarily, but the moment passes. I just want to Go Somewhere and Lie Down. I slide further into my seat in order to become as horizontal as possible without actually collapsing onto the floor and, as I pass into an altered state one might call Literature Fatigue, I realise, too late, I'm succumbing to a room full of Sulphur.

Sulphur is known as the king of remedies. This is because, in its material state, it is responsible for producing approximately three thousand symptoms and therefore, according to the homeopathic principle of like curing like, is able in homeopathic doses to cure just as many. However, for the sake of brevity and to encapsulate its essence, Sulphur symbolises the point at which the mind created the delusion that it was separate from the body. In an evolutionary sense, this may be the point at which sickness began.

The typical Sulphur type is described as the 'ragged-trousered philosopher.' Prone to flexing the intellectual muscles at the expense of personal hygiene, Sulphur is also prone to, well, being prone. The favoured position is recumbent.

The favoured pastime is theorising. The favoured sound is of their own voice.

Physically, the action of Sulphur is centrifugal and, like the eruption of volcanic matter, it encourages toxins to rise to the surface, producing discharges which are messy, itchy, smelly and, in contrast to the yellow of the material sulphur, usually very red. The Sulphur patient may have skin problems, lung problems, liver problems, bowel problems, sweat problems and, quite possibly, mental problems. As the energy concentrates itself in the intellect, the normal body processes suffer from inactivity and lack of reaction. As the brain gets over-loaded, there is a tendency to lose the thread and become absent-minded and eventually, paradoxically, incapable of rational thought.

The homeopathic world is full of Sulphurs. They are the ones doing all the research, writing the books, trying to explain to those of us who are just doing it anyway how homeopathy works. They are the ones giving over-priced seminars on why their particular method of prescribing is the one that will revolutionise my practice. They are the ones spending entire afternoons in online chat groups debating the optimum diameter of a sugar dragee. They are the ones who encourage dogma in an attempt to make the world fit in with their systems, their theories, their ideas. The fact that this is often at the expense of the patient's well-being is irrelevant to them.

Samuel Hahnemann, the founding father of homeopathy and therefore, inevitably, Sulphur to the core, once exhorted us all to 'have no theories.' I like the bare-faced cheek of this and it endears Sam to me, despite my having to acknowledge that it is, in itself, a theory.

The lecture has finished. It's Q & A time. The audience now recognises its chance to shine yet there are no real questions posed to The Writer, more a series of pretentious comments from the floor regarding abstraction, social delineation, radical verse-forms, and a spirited defence of the misogyny which pervades Lawrence's work.

Jessie's muttering something about deciding not to mix her gene pool with The Writer's after all. I tell her she never had a chance anyway, not with all these publishing maidens gagging for a quick one in the foyer, and suggest we just make for the exit and be first in line for the plonk. I can tell by her lack of reaction that she's disappointed, both in The Writer and in me. We don't fit with her idea of how it's meant to be. I want to cheer her up so I seize the moment and, rousing myself from my position halfway under the chair, wave my fist in the air and cry, "Better Passion and Death than any more of these Isms!" There is a shocked silence as I grab Jessie and we slither cravenly towards the door.

"What came over you?" she says, once we're downstairs, clutching cheap rioja in our red sweaty paws. "I never knew you could be, like, that embarrassing."

"It's a quote – from Lawrence, as in D.H. – I was being clever, actually." In an attempt to distract her, I point towards the window, "Look! Outside. It's beautiful."

We crunch our way down a silvery Strand arm-in-arm, the intense cold annihilating the sulphurous fumes still emanating from the Courtauld, the snow like a blank sheet of paper inscribed with our footprints, letting us make our mark on the world.

"Here's another quote for you," I offer. "'The wise man believes in nothing.'"

"Who said that?"

"It doesn't matter."

"Courtauld. Caught cold. Think I'll catch a bus instead," she says, giggling at her own wit and brilliance.

Better than being caught napping, I think lazily as I trundle towards Charing Cross – my breath leading the way home in swirling hieroglyphs, like snowflakes, impossible to pin down.

Class Warfare

Alice, one of my students, is presenting a case. She's managed to forget to ask several vital questions during the case-taking and is realising that she's now got the choice of owning her inadequacy or bluffing. I know what I'd do in the circumstances, having bluffed my way through several clinical hours during my own training, but I keep quiet. I believe this is what a good teacher should do. Pointing out someone's shortcomings is never the way to draw out the best in them, is it? Nurturing what is special in each person is the essence of education, isn't it? However, Alice is not leaving me much room for magnanimity. As I continue to listen to her increasingly wayward diagnosis, prognosis and probably neurosis, I'm aware that Sibylle, the extremely organized, meticulous note-taker of the group is tapping her pen on the side of her nose, just desperate for a chance to butt in and make Alice look foolish. I have to take charge.

"Okay," I say, "let's look at what we know here rather than what we assume. Let's just take what information the patient *has* given."

This is how I operate, working with what I have. The danger for students is that they always want to add more, bringing their own issues into the picture and thereby muddying the case.

Alice begins rambling again about the patient's menstrual irregularities being an expression of her power struggle with her mother. Sibylle is looking sour. Jamal is looking out of the window and Dorothy is breastfeeding her 6 month old baby, which leaves her without a free hand to take notes.

"... And anyway," Alice concludes, almost defiantly, "I think she needs Lycopodium."

As we're nowhere near the point of deciding on a remedy – as we are, in fact, still floundering in the swamp of Alice's attempt to disguise her mistakes – I need to draw the discussion back to some kind of overview of the case. However, I find myself suddenly irritated with Alice and her pretence that she knows what she's doing when she most clearly does not.

"There's no Lycopodium here," I say, gesturing towards her notes with a dismissive wave.

Alice looks crushed. Sibylle looks smug. Jamal looks bored. Dorothy looks for the baby's rattle which has fallen behind the sofa.

Lycopodium Clavatum is a remedy made from the club moss. Unlike the obviously poisonous plants such as Aconite, Belladonna or Nux Vomica, Lycopodium is an inocuous little thing. Inert in its natural state, classified somewhere between the mosses and the ferns, it has long, straggly stems from which protude erect, scaly spikes.

The mental picture of Lycopodium as a homeopathic remedy is one of lack of confidence covered up with bravado. The indeterminate nature of the plant is reflected in a diffidence which, given the right conditions, can turn very prickly. Terrified that their shortcomings will be exposed, Lycopodium patients will appear extremely self-possessed, charming and accommodating when dealing with those they perceive to be at a greater advantage, either at work, or when socialising. They bluff their way through such situations, driven by a fear of failure. Conscientious to a fault and fixated on their ability to perform, they will become distraught if corrected or shown-up. Wary of conflict due to a deep-seated cowardice, they can however become monstrous bullies when they feel safe. There is, then, a facility for biting sarcasm and unkindness towards those whom they consider to be weaker than themselves. Not for nothing is it renowned as a great remedy for teachers.

The physical problems created by this uneasy struggle of the ego will often centre in the abdomen. There is bloating, flatulance, an intolerance of tight clothing. Homeopaths will tell you this is caused by the anxiety, though you may feel it's just your lunch. The liver is particularly affected and therefore symptoms will be on the right side of the body and will be worse between 4 and 8 pm, when the liver reaches its lowest point of activity. There is often a craving for sugar at this time. The patient may have weak muscles or weak circulation. There is an inadequacy of function which reflects, or maybe leads to, the sense of inferiority on the psychological plane.

I launch into Alice, telling her that she has completely missed the essence of the case. As I watch her humiliation manifest in her reddening cheeks, I know that I am not handling this well but I just don't seem to be able to stop. Aware that she is doing her best, as Alice always does, I find it impossible to desist from criticising her just enough so that the group is in no doubt who is top dog. I kind of despise myself and wonder why I feel the need to be so harsh. Superficially, it's in order that Alice will become a good homeopath but underneath I have the horrible suspicion that I just enjoy knowing more than she does.

A small voice in my head is trying to suggest that actually I must be a lousy teacher if I haven't yet coached Alice properly in case taking methods. I refuse to listen to it. Sibylle is nodding eagerly at everything I say and I kind of despise her too, in the moment, for colluding with me. The counter-transference is so powerful now that, although I'm firing on all cylinders intellectually, I feel a weakness in my belly and a weariness in my legs which I recognise as being signals from my body that I need a cup of tea and a biscuit. I look at the clock. It's 4:15.

"Could you put the kettle on, Jamal?" I say, knowing he'll appreciate the chance to escape the tension for a few minutes. As he makes for the door, he accidentally kicks the sofa. The vibration wakes the baby, who farts loudly. Dorothy apologises on the baby's behalf and I reflect, for the thousandth time, on the ability of life to imitate art. I now have a constricting pain in my right temple, and my jeans feel too tight. Sibylle offers to hold the baby while Dorothy catches up with her notes. I look at Alice's defensive posture, all curled in on herself with her arms folded. Softening slightly, and ignoring the desire to belch, I lower myself onto the chair.

"Don't worry," I say, "you'll get the information next time you see her." Alice blinks at me through her fringe.

"And in the meantime," I continue, my magnanimous self returning to the room in increments, "let's hear your reasons for wanting to give her Lycopodium."

Jamal returns with the tea. I'm pleased to note he's remembered the biscuits. I do train them well, after all.

Squaring Up To The Paper Tiger

I'm in a combative mood. I'm honed. I'm primed. I'm mad as hell and I'm not going to take it anymore. I'm snarling, I'm growling, I'm moving in for the attack. And then my sword goes clunk against our precious 1950's chandelier with the twelve glass shades and Alistair, my tai chi teacher, hmmms a bit and says, "Maybe you need to redirect your energy towards the tip of the sword and stop trying to take my head off."

"Look," I say, exasperated, "you've only been teaching me for fifteen years. I mean, it's not as if I'm good at this or anything. I think you need to redirect your ability as a teacher and stop trying to pretend that it's so easy."

"Remember, you and the sword are one," Alistair continues. "Centre yourself in the lower tan tien. Which, may I remind you, rhymes with ab-do-men. Three finger widths below the navel. Then move your chi down the sword."

I take the kittens into the garden for the first time. Violet, who has been practising on any available indoor surface, is up a tree before I know it and peering over the fence into Erroll's beautifully tended undergrowth.

"Come down immediately, Violet!" I command, in a firm, maternal way.

She looks at me as if to say, "You must be joking. I now know what I am. I'm a cat."

Cosmo, her larger, more timid brother, lurks tentatively at the foot of the tree, his nose almost unable to cope with the delicious, disorientating aromas of the outdoors.

"Alistair! Quick!" I shout, "Violet's going over the fence."

Alistair is in my kitchen, recovering from the rigours of teaching me by making a pot of green tea.

"She's a cat," he calls back through the open window, unmoved by the urgency in my voice. "She'll be fine."

I brave the brambles to try and get hold of Violet who is now on the roof of the lean-to, ready to launch herself on to a dangerous world.

"But she's so little… the foxes… help… what if…"

Violet is playing pouncing games with the forsythia. She's swerving away from my outstretched hand. She's playing with me and my fear.

"Let go," a voice in my head is urging. "Just trust. Just let go."

Cosmo waits at the foot of the tree.

Fear and anger are two emotions which seem to come as a package. Or rather, underneath the anger, one usually finds a fear. And the fear is invariably a fear of loss. In my many years of studying tai chi I have had to confront this fear of loss in myself over and over again – loss of pride (getting pushed around); loss of balance (falling over); loss of ego (becoming one with the sword). In my homeopathic practice, having conquered my fear of loss of face (possibly giving the wrong remedy), I have encountered many kinds of anger which I have been required to contain on behalf of the patient while we searched together for the fear beneath. Only once has that anger been directed at me and, for a few sticky moments, I was confronted with fear of the loss of my front teeth. So far, not one of my patients has ever asked me whether I'm angry. Lucky for them, or they might have to encounter fear of loss of illusion (my homeopath is a super-being, beyond mere emotion).

There are many remedies in the homeopathic materia medica which we can use to treat anger, its causes and its effects. Also, we have a whole repertoire of remedies for fear. How is this possible? The world of allopathic medicine, fearing loss of everything it bases itself on, insists that it isn't. In order to shore up its edifice, it maintains that the body is simply a machine which reacts. Are we okay with that? I don't think so.

If you are reading this, if you are alive, I imagine you have at least once experienced the bodily sensation of fear – maybe in the churning of your stomach, or the pounding of your heart, or your knees going weak, or trembling, shivering. You've probably also experienced anger one way or another – getting hot, or feeling constricted in the throat, or clenching your muscles, grinding your teeth etc. These feelings originate in the body well before the mind labels them. The substances which provoke such adverse bodily responses (mainly poisons of one kind or another) will, if given homeopathically, also address the attached emotion. This is because homeopathy, like all holistic healing systems, operates on the premise that the mind and body are two manifestations of the same process. Biology and biography are intertwined.

Alistair appears with the tea to find me up a ladder, Violet in my arms. He puts the tea tray down, takes her from me and places her gently on the grass. She looks around for a few seconds, checks to see if Cosmo's still there, blinks at

Alistair and disappears like a rocket back up the tree. Alistair shrugs, and starts pouring. I glower at him.

"There's a tai chi festival near Paris in July," he says, not looking at me. "Wanna drive down there for the weekend?"

I hesitate, still halfway up the ladder, watching Violet's tail disappearing through the leaves.

"Ask me again tomorrow," I reply. "Right now I can't think of anything worse than a bunch of French martial arts enthusiasts telling me to let go."

"I think you'll find the correct term is lachez prise," Alistair says through a mouthful of green tea leaves. I imagine the tip of my sword piercing his skull and make a mental note to give him a remedy for smugness at the earliest opportunity. He gazes into the middle distance.

I realise that my position on the ladder is unstable to say the least and reluctantly climb down. Cosmo rubs himself against my ankles, purring loudly. I sit on the grass, stroking his soft, warm fur. His sweetness disarms me totally and the horrible confusion of fear and anger with which I have been wrestling dissolve into something pure and formless.

Alistair smiles.

"Love is an act of daring, you know," he says.

"Hard if one's a scaredy-cat," I reply.

"And fear is just something the mind has made up and is, therefore, untrue. A paper tiger."

The branches creak as Violet works her way back down to earth, Cosmo, Alistair and me. She licks my hand.

"Look at her, Alistair," I say. "Am I imagining it, or is she grinning?"

"Even warriors need a sense of humour," he replies.

I sheath my sword, the kittens lunging helpfully at its tassels – initiating a fraying process which I accept as probably being the start of an ongoing project. Alistair stretches cat-like on the grass.

Waiting For God

The window-cleaner finds me in.

"Hel-lo," he drawls with a kind of sarcastic surprise, "Fancy seeing you here. Been a while. That'll be seventy five pounds, please."

He flourishes his mandatory window-cleaner's notebook and stubby pencil.

"And I'm not taking plastic this quarter. It's bad for my karma."

I laugh, wearily.

"How you been keeping anyway? Got your current husband last time I knocked. At least, that man, you know, answered in his dressing-gown..."

"Brian," I say, "I haven't got seventy five pounds in cash right now."

"He didn't have any money, neither. You look a bit peaky," he continues. "How's work?"

"Oh..." I watch the drips fall from his rubber gloves, "...feel a bit drained."

"'Ere," he says, "have you been talking to anyone lately who may have been tampering with your energy? Think back, you know, made you feel tired at the time?"

"It's possible." A line-up of recent patients flashes before me. "Possible, yes..."

"Well, first you got to make sure you put on a cloak of protection, innit?"

He narrows his eyes, sizing me up.

"Then, you got to close down all your chakras one by one, starting from the crown, you know what I'm saying?"

"Right."

"And if that don't work..."

He leans towards me, brandishing his squeegee.

"...If that don't work, poke 'em with a big stick and tell 'em to piss off."

On my way back from the cash point, I stop at the newsagents. Torn between reading about Angelina Jolie's lesbian lust romp in The Sun and Michelle Obama's inappropriate hugging in The Times, I wonder which paper will be more persuasive in its efforts to cajole me to pass judgement on these icons of modern womanhood. I give up and reach for a copy of Psychic News. As I proffer some coins in payment, I notice Sayeed has a greyish pallor to his skin and his shoulders are all hunched up. I raise my eyebrows, questioningly.

"My tooth has been extracted," he says, handing me my change. "It is not good I am feeling."

"Here," I give him some Arnica from my permanent handbag supply. "This'll help."

"Many blessings," he bows to me before taking it. "I think you know something difficult and valuable."

Returning home, I call my phone company about a dodgy internet connection. My contact, "Hello my name is Stephanie. Welcome to Server Of Your Choice. How may I be of assistance today?" sounds defunct, like a battery in decline.

"I just buried my mother," she says, suddenly cutting off my explanation of my current cyber complaint. "I shouldn't be at work at all."

"So you're not in a call centre in Hyderabad, then?" I enquire, trying to keep things light.

"No, Ongar," she replies. "The nurses were wonderful at the end."

While we talk about the meaning of death and loss and motherhood, (Stephanie's childless so far but hopes that she and Andy will make a go of it and, who knows, maybe try IVF), and I offer a few suggestions of remedies for acute grief, I try to remember if 'This call may be recorded for training purposes' was included in her welcoming speech. As I hang up, I don't know whether to be more disturbed by the conversation itself or by the frequency with which conversations like this one jump out at me when I think I'm doing something else. I decide that what is really disturbing is that I'm not really disturbed at all. So homeopathy doesn't confine itself to the consulting room. Get over it.

Ricky, my seven year old son, is at home, having refused to go to school. He says he needs a day off. Apart from accompanying me to the newsagent, he's been bouncing around the house all morning and is probably hungry. I invite him to join me for cheese toasties.

Picking up Psychic News in his greasy little fingers and smearing melted cheese all over the back cover, he flicks through it in silence, then looks at me.

"Why've you bought this?" he demands, with his mouth full.

"Well, I was thinking about developing my psychic powers."

"Why?"

"So I can read your mind and find out where you hide your sweets."

"Yeah, but Mum..." he swallows the last of his toastie and licks his lips, "you're not psychic – you're psycho."

After lunch, I walk round the garden, accompanied by the cats. As we inspect the weeds together, Marjorie from next door leans out of an upstairs window.

"I just heard my workshop on the Dark Feminine's been cancelled," she hollers. "A'int that a bitch!"

The cats show their appreciation of Marjorie's unintended irony by scarpering under the ceanothus. I'm left alone in the middle of the lawn, trying to think of a reply.

Marjorie is dangerously close to falling out of the window now as she rails against the fates and the funding cuts.

"And another thing, Erroll's got piles. Got any pills in your magic box for a pain in the arse?"

As I look up at Marjorie's gleaming windows, I wonder how much cash she's handed over to Brian today. Before I can reply, the phone rings.

"Later, Marjorie," I wave, and hurry back into the house.

It's my 2:30 patient, Frida, on her mobile. She's been standing on the doorstep for several minutes.

Apologising profusely and leading the way to my consulting room, I find Ricky has emptied the entire contents of his crayon drawer on the stairs.

"Nice to know your kids are just as bad as mine," Frida remarks. "Artistic, is he?"

It transpires during our session that Frida has lost her job, and is covered in boils. Is there a link? Possibly. What can I, the homeopath, do about it? Not charge her, of course.

"It's ok, Frida," I reject her proffered cheque, "have this one on me."

Frida seems to be fighting off the urge to kiss my feet. I tuck them under my chair.

As she leaves she mentions a spiritualist church in Camberwell that she has been attending. Apparently it's a hot ticket to another dimension.

"What can you do if you're not saved?" she says.

Teatime. Ricky has finally been allowed to turn on the TV. I squint at my unkissed feet over my cup of Earl Grey, wondering if this would be a good moment to call the College of Psychic Studies. I'm just about to pick up the phone when it rings. Reading far too much into this, I half expect it to be the College of Psychic Studies calling me. Instead, it's my brother. He's got tickets for Waiting For Godot at the Barbican. We arrange to meet at the bar.

As my daughter, Tina, arrives home to Ricky-sit. I peer in the mirror and take a quick inventory. Cloak of protection? Decidedly worn. Chakras closed down? Hard to tell. Big stick? Could take my Tai Chi sword but doubtful would get it past Barbican ushers.

At the station I drop off some remedies with Leroy, who's been standing in a wind tunnel for many months, selling The Big Issue. He's just heard he's got a flat and is quietly ecstatic. After discussing the relative merits of the Ikea sprung mattress as opposed to a nice bit of foam and getting an update on his arthritis, I ask him how he's managed to, literally, keep standing – given the state of his hips and the refusal by London Transport to allow him to move out of the wind and onto the station forecourt.

"I been speakin' to God every day, an' he been tellin' me, 'Leroy, change is a gonna come.'" He looks up to the heavens, which are full of twinkling red lights on their way to and from Heathrow.

"Really?" I say. "So, it's one to God today, then?"

Leroy tuts at my feeble attempt at irreverence and diverts his attention toward the crowd of commuters flowing up the stairs. I realise, simultaneously, that I'm cramping his style and have missed my train.

My brother, Sam, is slumped at a table next to an elderly couple. He's sweating benignly.

"Thought you weren't going to make it. I've been waiting for ages."

"Good." I plonk myself down on the remaining vacant chair. "I'm sure Beckett would be very gratified."

I accept the offer of a large gin. I feel exhausted.

"So, how are you, Sis?"

"Dunno. Found myself envying a Big Issue seller a while back. Is that a good thing?"

The elderly couple are staring at us. Wrapping my protective cloak around me with a psychic swirl, I glare at them and they look away.

"People are always telling me that I have a very rewarding job," I say, a bit too loudly. "I can't imagine why."

"Oh shit." Sam fumbles in his pockets while rising from his chair. "Looks like I'm in for a bumpy night."

He pulls me up and waves the tickets in my face.

"These were really hard to get, you know."

Later, Sam and I wander down Moorgate towards Bank station, playing a stupid game which involves improvising Godot-like conversations and trying to out-do each other in an edgy, sibling way. He definitely has the upper hand, which feels all too familiar.

Dodging beggars, drunks, (at one point Sam trips over a dog on a string which sends me into paroxysms of cruel laughter until I realise the dog owner thinks I'm laughing at the dog and not just trying to get my own back on the brother who is more clever than me), we reach the corner of Princes Street and stand contemplating the night as it heaves its way through this wretched town.

"I'm thinking about developing my psychic powers," I say.

Sam, assuming this is still part of the game looks at me as if I just broke the rules.

"No, really, time-out. It's like I need a sign. Some kind of cosmic feedback, some reassurance that I'm doing the right thing with my life, that I'm on the right path, that the universe is..."

"Do me a favour," he scoffs. "Weren't you listening at all?"

He takes my hands in his and gently squeezes them as he whispers in my ear, "Sometimes a carrot is just a carrot."

Then he throws a glance at the alternative sleeping bag community settling down around us for the night, digs into his pockets for some change and chucks the coins into the hat of the nearest crustie.

"I think that's checkmate, vingt-et-un and goal to me, don't you?"

Home again, I pick up the by now exceedingly scruffy Psychic News which has materialised at my bedside despite my having left it downstairs next to the phone. Ricky's greasy fingerprints have been joined by an elaborate doodle that loops down from the capital P of Psychic and crawls across a photo of a woman who is this month's profiled medium.

She is wearing biro spectacles, a fright wig and bushy moustache, drawn with gusto and obliterating any gravitas her portrait may have once contained. She reminds me a bit of Einstein. Suspecting Tina's hand, I remember that Einstein once said we have two choices – to live life as if nothing were a miracle or to live life as if everything were a miracle.

I place the magazine into the recycling bin, and hunt for my copy of the play, thinking I'll look for a line to text to Sam before he goes to sleep – a riposte, although, carrots notwithstanding, that may be cheating.

There are so many possibilities: 'Tomorrow, when I wake or think I do, what shall I say of today?' or 'When I think of it all these years but for me... where would you be?' or 'May one inquire where His Highness spent the night?'

I try and work out some variations on these themes, such as 'What shall I do with all these tomorrows?' still smarting from being upstaged. Then, capitulating to the notion that making a pillow of words for my head is the reason I sometimes have trouble sleeping, and that trying to get the better of Sam can wait, I succumb to a silent stage direction from my eyelids. Sam's probably a goner anyway, by now.

'Let us do something while we have the chance! It is not every day that we are needed.'

Biological Welfare

London. September 2001. I look up whenever a plane flies overhead, just to check. People are now dying from inhaling anthrax in the post-room. There is the expectation of attack, not only from the sky but from deadly diseases unleashed into the atmosphere.

In my private practice, I have a few patients who work in the City. Since the Twin Towers came down, they have been the most affected. They go about the daily business of rearranging money in a fog of fear. It sits in the consulting room with us. I ask it to speak.

"I just keep thinking, will I be next? Is it going to happen today?"

"I don't want to get up, let alone go to work. I'm a sitting duck."

"How can I concentrate on my job when I feel as if I could be hurtling through the sky, on fire, at any moment?"

"I sit on the Tube waiting to be gassed."

"I don't want to die because I work in a bank."

As I listen, I check myself for signs of contagion. Maybe it's my low-rise job, my natural perversity, or maybe I'm dangerously out of touch with reality but I don't seem to be lost in the fog with them. Okay, there's the looking up whenever a plane flies overhead thing but I can put that down to curiosity, can't I? The truth is I'm just not as vulnerable as they are. What they need is protection.

Kate, my friend and fellow homeopath, calls to compare notes. She's hearing the same thing from her patients. She's had an idea.

"We make a remedy from homeopathic anthrax, label it Biological Welfare and give it to them to put in their pockets."

"Like a talisman?"

"Exactly."

"Great. Can you come up with something to deflect fear of planes?"

"Airborne assault? Not really our field is it, unless you're talking wasps, bees..."

I look up anthrax in the homeopathic materia medica. 'It was first introduced as a remedy by Lux the veterinarian long before the experiments of Pasteur. The potentised bacillus is the best remedy for the disease from which it is obtained.' Interestingly, among the mental symptoms listed are 'Thinks she feels death approaching' and also 'Disinclined to work.'

I need to explain. A potentised bacillus is a homeopathic remedy made from a disease-causing agent. It may come as a surprise to those of you who thought we just crushed up flower petals and added lots of water that we can make a remedy from anything, literally anything at all. The most harmful disease, the most sinister poison, the most disgusting matter, (rotting beef is one of my favourites), can be turned by the process of homeopathic dilution and succusion into a curative medicine. How can this happen? Because, as Shakespeare said, 'In poison there is physik.'

The talisman idea works a treat. While we're at it, we add smallpox, leprosy and botulism to the anthrax, diluted to the thirtieth potency which means it now contains the dynamic energy of the diseases but any trace of the material substances disappeared several dilutions ago. (We order this from the homeopathic pharmacy, legal dept. please note. We don't, I repeat, don't have any deadly diseases in our possession.)

None of the patients ever get to take the remedy because the biological warfare doesn't actually happen, but they all report a sense of comfort from knowing that, in the event, they could, possibly, DO SOMETHING to antidote the effects. The fog lifts. Life goes on.

London. March 2003. The Iraqis are bombed 'in order to make the world a safer place.' I'm still refusing to be scared, figuring that the whole mess feeds on fear and I don't want to be part of the meal. I notice that, among my patients at the Community Centre on the other side of town, not one person mentions a fear of terrorism. They don't have time, life on the edge being a fully occupying force. The City types are on the phone again, though.

London. December 2004. The 'War on Terror' continues. We're warned repeatedly that the capital is an inevitable target, yet the emphasis has shifted away from biological weapons and back to bombs. The bottles of Biological Welfare are probably all lost, broken or gathering dust at the back of a drawer.

London. July 2005. The inevitable happens. Four bombs explode and London closes down. I'm at work when I hear the receptionist mumbling about "serious fatalities," whatever that means. I get a crackly call from Ricky's teacher, then the line goes dead. As I can't get through to anyone on the land line and all the mobile networks are down, I hurry home. There are no trains.

In a taxi crawling along the Old Kent Road, I encounter a driver who tells me he never stops for blacks anymore. According to him, they're all the same and cause nothing but trouble.

"Do you really think this is the time to be looking for reasons to hate people?" I say to his back as he rants on, oblivious. Exasperated, I ask him to stop the cab and I hop on an equally slow-moving bus. The passengers are all talking to each other in a concerned way and it's interfering with my need to only have one thought right now, which is to get home. I slide off the bus and walk the last half mile through subdued streets which, although clogged with traffic, seem strangely quiet and echo my own sense of numb detachment from the reality of the news. Finally, I make it through the front door, grab the phone and eventually ascertain that both Ricky and Tyrone, my older son, are being driven home by friends. Tina is still in bed, sleeping peacefully through a historic moment.

Knowing I won't be able to relax until the boys are back, I distract myself by tidying up my workroom. As I pick up a pile of papers waiting to be filed, a photo flutters to the floor. It's a picture I tore from a newspaper in September 2001 and kept for some reason. A head and shoulders of Osama Bin Laden looking straight into the lens. It's blurry, probably enlarged from a telephoto with consequent loss of definition. He looks ethereal, insubstantial, as if he is no longer fully of this world . Reports at the time suggested his health was failing. Chronic kidney problems. This intrigues me greatly as, according to Chinese medicine, the kidneys are particularly affected by fear. Loss of bladder control in response to adrenalin release is the acute manifestation[2]. To develop a chronic kidney disease, one may have experienced repeated or continual fear. Terror, even? How ironic to imagine the great fear-monger of the age being himself a victim of the fog.

"What is it that frightens you, Osama?" I whisper. "Do you feel your edges blurring with the Almighty or are you scared that, in the final reckoning, you just won't be considered righteous enough? Do you want to be a spectre forever, or do you long to be impaled upon your own truth?"

Surprisingly, the picture answers. It's not Osama's voice, of course, I'm not deluded, but a rumbling of consciousness. It says: "Fear is the absence of Love. I am the result, not the cause. Your job, if you think you're up to it, is to open your heart and spread the disease of Love. Label it if you must, but please don't expect it to fit in a bottle."

London. The Present. The USA, with grave fixity of purpose, continues to tighten (or is it bludgeon) the rhetoric of patriotism, and appears to silence Osama by having him murdered at point blank range. Global recession increases the divide between the haves and the have-nots. The media still crank up the fear quotient on a daily basis but the threat is now monetary. Fearing planes overhead is a thing of the past, and I can't quite remember what that felt like. Anthrax hasn't been mentioned in a good long while.

However, one of my patients at the commumity centre, a Muslim, tells me that her husband was arrested for having

---

2 In Chinese medicine the kidneys and adrenal glands are considered as one.

a beard and wearing a Palestinian scarf. He's a short-order cook in an American diner in the West End. He spent a night in the cells.

Kate takes me to a party in a huge house, a few streets away from my own. There are so many people in the hallway that I endure several minutes of breathless squeezing to get through to the other end. Everyone looks slightly mad, boggle-eyed, grinning or glaring or leering, and the lighting is horrible. I'm at the top of a flight of stairs leading to a crowded basement from which there may be no other exit.

I stop in my tracks and say, "No."

"What do you mean, 'No'? It'll be fine. Go on."

"No. I'm leaving. This is like the seventh circle of hell. I want to go."

I turn and push my way back along the hallway to the front door – a ridiculously wide, late Victorian portal, scuffed white paint and stippled glass panels.

As I pass into the quiet midnight street and look up at the sky, a flock of geese are silhouetted in a perfect arrowhead formation against the glare of the moon and the street light.

Kate follows me.

"What are you looking at?" she says, tracking my gaze, then gasps. "Wow. I didn't know geese flew at nightime."

"When Tina was little," I say, "I used to tell her that elephants could fly but they only did it at night because they were shy, like her. Their ears became wings and their legs folded up like an aeroplane undercarriage. But only at night, when no-one was looking."

"That'd be hard to achieve in South London," says Kate, "especially round here."

She indicates the house behind us. "Are you coming back inside?"

"I don't think so." I shake my head, loosening the crick in my neck.

"I'm loath to ask the obvious, but have you thought of taking a remedy for your obvious acute claustrophobia?"

"I'm not claustrophobic. There's too many people. It's a fire risk."

"Uh-huh," Kate says, "O-kay... And in the event of a fire, or explosion or well, while we're at it, people dying of asphyxiation, or being trampled, a terrorist attack maybe – as we know, South London parties tend to go that way, particularly when they're at my friends' houses – woudn't it be incumbent on you, as a homeopath, to attend at the scene?"

"Risk my life to save others? I don't think I signed up for that. I have children."

"You're right," she says. "Come on, let's go. Can I drive? I haven't for ages."

Kate can't get the car started but insists on keeping at it and manages to flood the engine.

"That's it. We can't go anywhere for a while. Shall we go back to the party?" she says.

I offer to try. It starts immediately. Kate looks at me whilst avoiding looking at me. I shrug.

"It's all about knowing how much pressure to apply, and when to stop," I say.

"That's very sagacious of you," she replies, shifting back into the driving-seat while I walk round to the other side of the car. There's a puddle in a pot-hole that I don't notice and step in, my shoe filling with water.

As we lurch towards my house, thankfully not too far, I sit with my legs and my fingers crossed, one damp, squelchy foot dangling, and pray that this time Kate won't confuse the brake with the accelerator or decide to do her hair in the rear-view mirror. The moon has disappeared behind a bank of cloud. I think of elephants poised on the runway of disclosure, and Osama still irksome in his grave, like a misprint on the page where nothing is written, as Kate finally, victoriously and charmingly, manages to crunch our getaway vehicle into a stuttering second gear.

I Make No Excuses

The plaintive strains of Dvorak's Piano Trio in E Minor sweep over me as I sit huddled next to my friend, Caz, in my local church. The heaters are on but a fierce, unseasonal little wind flits round our ankles, causing us to lean into each other for warmth.

We'll probably both start crying soon. One of us will cultivate a moist-eyed drip and the other, acknowledging the cue in the symbiotic way only good friends of long-standing can, will reach for a tissue. Then we'll link arms, exchange a watery smile and, with a warm glow, remember all the other times we've done this, all the other occasions when we've let the music play upon our hearts. It's amicable, therapeutic, classic even.

As I marvel at the fluid concentration of the musicians in front of me, engaged with themselves and each other in a seemingly effortless way, I realise with a start what it is that has been bothering me for several weeks. Or rather, I realise with a start that what has been bothering me for several weeks has a name. It's called Writer's Block.

A voice inside my head, sounding suspiciously like one of my old homeopathy teachers, immediately queries whether this is a revelation or a diagnosis. Given where I'm sitting, I'm open to the possibility of having been suffused with the divine. If it's a diagnosis, on the other hand, I just want to know the treatment.

Something has cleared in my brain. All those times lately when I've sat at my desk, playing on the keyboard of my computer in an effort to coax something readable, find a melody, tap a rhythm, locate a theme and then ended up pressing the delete button and turning to my inbox with a perplexed sigh – without realising it, I've been experiencing one of the greatest obstacles known to writers the world over. I've joined a club, founded on absence. Good Grief!

The atmosphere in the church seems to shift as my realisation coincides with the next item on the programme which features a wickedly dissonant viola performing something that can only be described as modern. It lends an air of cold menace to the draught rising up from the flagstones. As a future without being able to shape my imagination into words looms before me, I feel full of emptiness. Is this what the Taoist sages have been trying to teach me for two thousand years, or is it merely the start of my decline into middle-aged apathy?

"Caz,"I whisper, "I've got Writer's Block."

"Not now," she hisses out of the side of her mouth, "Have some respect. Tissue!" She sticks her hand out. I delve into my coat pocket and give her the whole packet. I've completely abandoned the idea of having a good cry. In fact, I can no longer hear the music at all. Now I know the name of my complaint, I want to be off. I need to find a cure. Instead, I wait for the interval.

I don't know if my neighbourhood is unique in featuring a crumbling church with attached wine bar, complete with a vicar who used to be the marketing manager for Air France. I don't know if it's making a difference to the size of the congregation, as I am not a churchgoer. What I do know is the Friday night concerts are packed.

As an example of creative thinking, Father Frank's efficient, if somewhat renegade, method of raising funds to repair the church roof must be admired. Sadly, his exposure to French culture has done nothing for the calibre of the wine he serves, and he is often plagued by nervous phone calls from the diocese but, all in all, Father Frank strikes me as someone who has given himself permission to do what it takes to clear a path through difficulty. He's gone round the block, as it were. I, on the other hand, strike myself as on a path to nowhere.

"Well, actually," Caz pulls a face as she downs a mouthful of something barely fit for a communion chalice, "I fail to see the problem. I mean, you're a homeopath not a writer so it's not important, is it, in the general scheme of things? In fact, it's probably a good thing, less of a distraction, you know, more time for study and CPD, less exposure to EMFS, reduced risk of RSI – you might even get your housework done occasionally. Oh look, there's Erroll and Marjorie. Do you want another drink?"

"But, Caz," I grasp her wrist as she turns to go to the bar, "I can FEEL the block. The blankness is tangible. I suddenly understand Nothing. And, even better, it's got a name."

She looks at me, pityingly.

"So what are you going to do, Little Miss Hemingway? Move to Havana, become an alcoholic, go fishing and blow your brains out? I don't think so."

As she totters off to buy more drinks, one of my patients, a hairdresser with the coincidentally afore-mentioned RSI, hoves into view. I feel dismissed by Caz. She has defined me in her terms and in doing so prevented a part of me from being heard, a part which undeniably exists but which she has a problem accepting due to the fact that she's maybe, basically, deep down, in spite of all this talk about Hemingway, simply illiterate. What else could it be? I feel silenced, voiceless, mute. As my patient advances towards me, I groan inwardly but make no sound.

Gayle, the hairdresser, introduces me to her husband, Derek, and they both sit down. Caz is flirting with Father Frank on the other side of the room. I try to catch her eye, but I can tell it's pointless. Derek fidgets with his wedding ring. He's probably heard all about me from Gayle and, now that we're face to face, he's probably trying to remember all those questions he thought of the first time she told him she'd been to see a homeopath; questions which deflected that niggling little fear he could feel eating away at a corner of his mind that his wife may be about to turn into someone he didn't recognise.

Gayle offers to buy me a drink. I glance over at Caz, who is hanging on Father Frank's arm, causing the blue-rinses to tut tut in arias of disapproval.

"Thanks, I'll have a spritzer."

Derek seizes his chance.

"Oh, so you drink alcohol, do you?" He can't disguise a smirk. "I thought you lot were all pure and stuff."

The banal predictability of this makes me want to point two fingers at my temple, pull an imaginary trigger and slump forward onto the table, my head in a pool of red wine. What would Derek say then?

"Just doing my bit for the church roof," I reply.

Gayle shakes her head.

"Father Frank's too much, ain't he? Did you know he, like, studied at the Paris Conservatory?" She rearranges the beermats, wincing. RSI no better then, I think.

"Get out of it!" Derek scoffs. "You tellin' me he went to school in a greenhouse? It's Conserva-Tw-arr, innit?"

His elongated consonants cause the arteries in his neck to bulge uninvitingly. His desire to belittle Gayle, which he may well have meant to leave at home but which, after many years of faithful service, has tagged along anyway, joins us at the table, and we all shift in our seats to make room.

"Right, then," Gayle says, more to the beermats than to Derek and I, "Spritzer, hmm, bit on the chilly side. Shame Father Frank don't do Bacardi, I could… "

"Nah, love. Makes your face all blotchy," Derek's gallantry insists.

She presses a ten pound note into his hand and he's off. I'm hoping Gayle is not going to mention anything about her health as we sit in silence for a few moments.

"Booked your holiday yet?" she enquires, eventually.

Some words from a poster in my son, Tyrone's, room insinuate their way into my frontal lobes. Something Ninja-ish. Something I meant to talk to him about. *'I make no excuses. My actions are my voice.'*

"Well, actually," I say, sounding strangely like Caz, "I had been planning a trip to Havana, but now I'm not so sure."

"Havana? Where's that, then? Somewhere in South America, innit?"

"Kind of," I agree.

"Derek and me's goin' to Hastings again. Bloody Hastings!"

I can feel Gayle willing me to indulge her pain but, hey, it's Friday night and I'm off duty. I have a perplexing desire for Derek to return soon and relieve me of this conversation.

I make no excuses…

"Sea air will do you good." I say. Gayle sighs.

As the five minute bell sounds, Derek reappears, having elbowed his way to the front of the bar in no time. Gayle sighs again and we clink our glasses together, Derek squinting at me.

"I got you a large one, Doctor." He grins.

"Fabulous." I grin back. "Shame there isn't time to drink it."

Caz returns, muttering something about dried up old biddies with no sense of humour.

"Oh," she says, taking in Gayle and Derek with an imperious blink. "Gayle. That's handy. I've been meaning to come and get my ends trimmed for ages. Got your scissors on you?"

Gayle is suddenly experiencing that hey, its Friday night, I'm off duty feeling for herself.

"Well, you'd best give me a tinkle, like, tomorrow... er..." she stutters.

"C'mon, missus," Derek is now panting with the effort of swallowing a glass of one of Father Frank's lowliest vintages in a single gulp, "business is business. Take her in the Lava-Tw-arr." He belches loudly.

Gayle turns to me, ignoring Derek yet again.

"So you two ladies know each other, or what?"

Is this my cue, the real reason I came here tonight? I feel an electric frisson, a ripple of something bright and clear and dangerous, willing me to speak. I could remind Gayle that her wrist will not get better until she changes her job, and add that even that may not be enough – she may need to change her husband. I could tell Caz that she's rubbish at listening, she's a lousy friend, and she ought to think about the precariousness of Father Frank's socio-religious experiment before giving full rein to her hedonistic impulses and shocking the matrons of the borough, probably his most generous donors. I could tell Derek that, from what I know of him from Gayle, he's in deep doo-doo unless he faces up to his need to turn women into martyrs and from what I can discern from my own observations he's a misogynistic control freak. The three of them are looking at me as if waiting for me to speak.

"Yes," I say, nodding with a fervour which gathers up all the electricity and connects it with something big and beyond reproach, "Yes, we do know each other, very well in fact. Caz is my best friend."

Father Frank is shooing the blue-rinses back into the church for another bout with culture. They twitter adoringly.

"Fancy," says Gayle. "After all these years."

My actions are my voice…

"And I hope you all enjoy the second half," I put my lukewarm spritzer on the table, "but me, I'm now going home to write."

"Aha," says Derek, "I had a feeling you was taking notes when I saw you sitting there with that big scowl on your face."

If Derek had a chin, I might now suggest he takes one on it.

"She's got Writer's Block," Caz says, with some authority, "which is a good thing because it means I may get to see her a bit more. Going home to write? For God's sake, you'll miss the Mozart. Father Frank gave me his handkerchief."

"Sweet," Derek says, "sweet as a nut."

I put on my coat.

"Call me," Caz whispers in my ear, "and don't stay up too late."

Gayle waves her sore wrist as I walk away.

I amble down the hill towards home, imagining I can still hear the music though it's probably just the crack addicts jamming in the park. How lucky we are to have Father Frank in our midst, I think. A true visionary.

I hope Tyrone will still be up so we can have a little ninja conversation before bed. My middle child, a straight-talking sixteen year old, he is the only one who has inherited my love of martial arts.

The house is quiet, so I thrust my arms into the darkness, shadows playing with my silhouette as I practice a few sword moves before turning on the light. Time to confront the word processor, I guess.

I decide it would be nice to have a little background music and, searching online for the Piano Trio in E minor, I find something for typists called the Dvorak keyboard. Its letters are in a different arrangement to QWERTY, purported to be more ergonomically sound and to reduce the risk of RSI.

If the pen really is mightier than the sword, the right keyboard may be the key to getting it right, I think. If I'm to make no more excuses, then my actions and my voice need to be as one – and what better to aid them than an expensive piece of hardware designed for secretaries.

"Only a bad writer blames her keyboard," my old homeopathy teacher admonishes as the piano music surges into the rapidly filling Nothingness. "Is that the action of a voice that deserves to be heard or are you just making another excuse?"

"I thought I'd left you behind at the church," I mutter.

"Well, apparently not," he replies, "though if you want me to go we could do a deal."

"What, more homeopathy, less writing?"

"No. Less resisting, more focusing on the facts."

"Meaning?"

"The 'obstacle to cure'," he says, "is a phenomenon we homeopaths encounter often. How about if the obstacle is the cure?"

"You mean the block is the way round itself. Ninja, baby!"

I flex my right wrist, my writing wrist.

"I'm not getting in the ring with you or Hemingway though," I add. "My wrist hurts. I've probably got the beginning of RSI. What if the block is telling me that the cure is to give up writing altogether?"

"If you could you be as creative with your prose as you are with your excuses, you may… "

The front door opens and Tyrone rushes in.

"Chill Out Now, Mum!" he says, "Ricky's safe! Don't Panic! We was at the cinema, and then he was hungry so I got him a takeaway. He's, like, hiding in the bushes. Can you go to the door and act all freaked so he can jump out at you and go boo or whatever. Just don't tell him it was me what told you…"

"Let me get this straight," I say, rising from my chair. "You've been out. To the cinema. With Ricky. And you didn't tell me. And he's outside. Alone. In the dark."

"Your phone was off, that concert you went to. I left you a message. You was unreachable."

As I open the front door, and Ricky leaps into my arms, laughing maniacally, and I pretend to have been really, really worried, I grapple with what to say next.

I make no excuses.

"Tyrone, I..."

"No school tomorrow, so he can stay up late, yeah? And on top of what you owe me for babysitting, there's the tenner I spent at the movie, and the takeaway after. But don't worry, Mum, you can give it me tomorrow."

Does he need to know I thought they were both upstairs fast asleep, though given that it's Friday night, why would they be? Is it really possible that I didn't check?

My actions are my voice.

"Tyrone, there's a poster on your wall. It says..."

Ricky's up on Tyrone's shoulders now, yelling "Snacks!" and I follow them as they lurch into the kitchen. The piano trio has ended so I switch off the computer before anyone can suggest a quick game of something, and make toast. Ricky's so hyper from excitement that conversation is a challenge, but I persist. I feel furtive, somehow, as if I'm about to be exposed as an imposter in my own home.

"How was the film?" I ask Ricky.

"Wicked. It was a 12," he says, "Wiiiickedddd!"

"And how did you get him in?" I ask Tyrone.

"Easy, Mum. I just told him to act like he was vertically challenged."

"And no-one stopped you? The ticket taker...?"

"No, Mum. It was well cool."

'WELL COOL!!!" Ricky yells in my face. How anyone could mistake him for...

"Have you been talking to Father Frank?" I ask.

"What, the God-botherer?" Tyrone replies. "Is it likely?"

Ricky flakes out on the floor and I tell Tyrone I'll give him even more money if he can get Ricky ready for bed and read him a calm, peaceful story.

While they wrestle their way up to the bathroom, I tidy – an action I fall into when I need to think. Then I turn the computer back on and, as the plaintive strains of Dvorak's Piano Trio in E Minor sweep over me once again, the noises from upstairs become more muted as I remember what it is I've been trying to say.

Dirty Bargains

Brixton, June. I walk down Railton Road, humming a little ditty by Eminem with which I am intimately acquainted thanks to Tyrone's habit of playing it relentlessly at home lest we forget that, although we may think we live in leafy suburbia, the ghetto is just around the corner. As I move out of the path of an oncoming wino, I half-trip over some picture frames left on the pavement in a discarded heap. The glass is missing, but they look like oak. I pull the two least damaged ones from the pile. They're big, beautiful, covered in cobwebby stuff but otherwise sound. With one on each shoulder, I reckon I should be able to manage as far as Max's flat, then a cab home. I gird myself and look at my watch. I'm late, but Max will not have noticed.

The lift splutters to a halt on the top floor. In the corridor there is a strong smell of urine, and smoke from a recent spliff hangs heavily in the air. Max's door is open, and I struggle through with my picture frames to find him at his computer, his back towards me and the outside world. He turns his head, and looks me up and down. I realise from his expression that I'm probably a bit dishevelled, sweaty from the effort of lugging two large rectangles of oak all the way down Railton Road.

"Be with you in a minute," he says, turning back to the computer. "So, what you got there, anyway?"

I feel exhausted from my exertion, and hope the throbbing in my right shoulder will stop soon. I'm grimy and damp, yet part of me is alight with the promise of my latest find.

"Dirty bargains," I reply, and am just about to start recounting the lucky stumbling over of these beautiful pieces of wood when he slams his palm down on the desk.

"Fantastic!" he exclaims. "I've been sitting here all morning searching for the language of the city and you walk in with the perfect phrase."

He's still got his back to me. I'm thirsty.

"D-i-r-t-y-b-a-r-g-a-i-n-s," he types.

"Do I get a credit?" I ask. "Do I at least get something to drink?"

After lunch, we sit on Max's balcony discussing his search for his birth mother. He now has the address where she currently lives but he's too scared to go there, or even write. He's filled in a lot of missing detail since we last met and leads me through a projected scenario of shock, recrimination, guilt, and continued psychic and emotional pain should he attempt to contact her. As I listen – trying to imagine what it's like to not know who your parents are, to lack a geanealogical context – I appreciate how hard it is to visualise absence. I settle for the image of a mantle-piece full of family photographs – except the photos themselves are missing, the frames are empty.

"Isn't it a little dangerous to sit with your back to an open door round here?" I ask. "Most people seem to have grilles and double mortice locks."

"What's the worst that can happen? I die in a hail of bullets?"

He smiles, and tries to manoevere his wheelchair past his plant pots and my outstretched legs. "Dessert?"

As I wheel him towards the kitchen, we pass my picture frames, propped up against his desk. I'd temporarily forgotten about my new acquisitions and feel a rush of pleasure at the sight of them. A moment later, I feel a stab of helplessness as I look over the top of Max's dark, curly head at his desk piled high with pamphlets on disability benefits and literature from The Adoption Society.

"Who was it who said the family is the void out of which you emerge and to which you must inevitably return in some kind of nihilistic surrender?" I murmer, scanning his bookshelves.

"Well, whoever it was I doubt they said 'kind of'," Max replies, running his finger through the cobwebby dust on top of one of the frames.

As he directs me towards the strawberries lying in a colander in the sink, I suddenly realise my mistake. It's not the empty space within the frame that's the problem for Max – he can fill any space with the sheer force of his beautiful, wise and intricate being. It's that the frame itself is missing.

One of the major areas of enquiry in a homeopathic case-taking is the patient's family medical history. No surprises there, as the acknowledgement of the relevance of inherited susceptibilities has resulted in the biggest scientific project of our time, the mapping of human genes. However, we homeopaths take the information our patients give us concerning their parents, grandparents and siblings and use it somewhat differently to the medics. The patterns which make sense to us are those concerning the function of energy, and we see relationships between different physical conditions and events which, in the reductionist mindset of allopathic medicine, are unconnected. The discernment of a thread moving through generations of a family helps us to understand the causes of illness and the obstacles to cure. The fact that homeopathy provides remedies to counteract these obstacles is one reason why it is so effective at treating chronic conditions, and why it is able to strengthen the individual, constitutional state.

Patients who have been adopted inevitably have a big blank in this area of their case notes. The past does not frame the present in the same way as for the rest of us. Although this matters a lot to them, for the homeopath it is a reminder that identity is not a fixed 'thing' but a fluid process.

When Max took the bullet in his spinal cord during a savage mugging, it may have made sense to have previously known that his mother had been a teenage junkie who had given him away because she feared her pimp would brutalise him, but would it have stopped the bullet? One function of energy is to be perverse and, consequently, destructive. Drug addiction and gun crime are homeopathic bedfellows as well as sociological ones. Was there an inevitability to Max's current situation beyond the rational, statistical map concerning street warfare and young black men in the inner city? Could homeopathy have intervened? To claim that it could is to invite ridicule from the reductionists but I've seen enough examples of destructive tendencies transform, through homeopathic treatment, into creative ones to wish I'd known Max before he was felled – like an oak tree in the forest.

"I'm giving you my frames," I say decisively, wiping strawberry juice from my chin.

"What for? I don't have any pictures."

"You're a work in progress. You can fill them with yourself. Or... maybe... one for each parent, or... before and after, or..."

Max laughs at my desperation. He's heard it all before, a thousand times.

"Rub my feet for me, will you. They get so swollen in the heat."

I raise one of his legs onto my lap and work my thumbs into the sole of his foot.

"Any idea when you'll be getting a transfer to the ground floor?"

"I've got to learn to appear less self-sufficent first. Hard, when I've been doing it all my life. I cope too well, it counts against me."

"Max, you're a playwright. Just be dramatic!"

"You're appallingly flippant sometimes, you know," he says. "Not much of a bedside manner."

I continue to knead his foot and his puffy ankle, reflecting on how far Max travels daily without even leaving his flat. I'm embarrassed by the memory of my tiredness as I carried the wooden frames through the street, a pleasant handicap to have had at the time and one of my own choosing.

"Look at it like this," I suggest. "Your mother had to make dirty bargains to survive. The currency she dealt in wasn't her choice. She did her best. Now you need to forgive, and to figure out what else you need in order to get out of the chair."

Surprised at my own lucidity and its emphatic quality, I replace his leg and go in search of a hammer and nails.

"The drill's in the cupboard by the front door," he calls out. "Next to the ladder."

Without pausing to imagine Max on a ladder, I busy myself choosing the ideal spots for the two frames. My presumption that I know what he needs gives me a vigour which sees them up in no time. They look faintly absurd of course, framing pieces of blank wall.

"Come and see," I call but he doesn't answer. He's fallen asleep in the sun. I find a pencil on his desk and write 'Max is here' on the wall inside one of the frames, '... and here' inside the other. Then I put the tools away, wash the dishes, shake the dust from my hair and get ready to leave.

Standing in the corridor, I debate whether to close the front door on my way out. My baser instincts tell me that I should, my finer ones instruct me to leave it open. Max sleeps on in the sun.

Something In The Water

We sit in the shade of a hibiscus tree by the Aegean, eating lunch. A huge crow appears loudly overhead. Ignored by the scavenging cats crouched at our feet, it creates a tremor in the branches which ripples down, unsettling the cutlery.

Carlo leans across the table, crumbling bread between his fingers as if to tease the flapping shadow above. It flies off with a brief, protesting cry.

"Did I ever tell you the story of Apollo and the crow?" He pauses, one eyebrow raised. I shrug.

"In the days when crows were white, Apollo charged one with the task of watching over Coronis, his pregnant girlfriend. He didn't trust her, you see. He knew how faithless women can be."

He pauses again. "Shall I go on?"

I gesture haphazardly for him to continue, and reach for the ouzo.

"Coronis found herself attracted to another man and gave herself to him. The white crow saw everything. When it reported back to Apollo, who was in Delphi at the time taking care of business, the god was so disturbed by the news that he threw a divine tantrum, a jealous rage full of darkness. It was so dark in fact, and so powerful, that the force of it changed the colour of the bird's feathers and from that day to this crows are not white, but black."

I push my plate of cuttlefish away, the cats observing closely. Carlo picks up a tentacle and slowly bites off the tip. I watch the line of his jaw, wondering at the random collision of energy and matter that has created such a perfect interruption of space.

"The gods were a dastardly lot." He smiles happily, as if he knows something I will never understand. "They treated women abysmally, it's true."

He takes another piece of fish from my plate. The cats scratch the ground in anticipation.

"Not only gods, but heroes also. For example, Peleus chased Thetis to the ends of the earth, so mad was he with desire, and, when he finally caught up with her in those waves down there, he assumed the form of a cuttlefish in order to trick her, to have his wicked way. And you know, of course, that the fruit of their union was Achilles."

"I've always had a soft spot for Achilles," I sigh.

He looks at me, ruefully.

"That's a terrible joke, even by your standards. It would be nice if you took me seriously now and again."

On this friendly isle, where humans, goddesses and sea creatures once intertwined, the idea of metamorphosis is never far away. As I shed my city skin, I find myself changing daily into a more primal being who doesn't care very much for the complexities of life. But I rouse myself slightly in my chair and scratch my head.

"Thetis was a very bad mother," I reply. "She dangled Achilles in the fire to try and make him immortal. She'd already lost six children working that particular stunt. Peleus, the nurturing father, had to snatch him from her, to rescue him from her mad ambition. Social services would have had a field day."

I sink back down, overcome by the effort of thought. Carlo licks the remains of the cuttlefish from his fingers.

"But it's interesting, isn't it," he says, "these stories of exchange and disguise, this… shape-shifting? What does it tell us about ourselves and our relationship with the world? What do you say?"

The crow flies in again from the south, its voice drowning out my lack of response. Carlo turns to look. The cats notice all the food has gone and defect to another table. Carlo turns back to me, his face full of light – like Apollo, I think, like a god kissed by the sun.

Later, having stopped for a drink at a café on the beach, we are accosted by an English woman who has overheard us talking about homeopathy. She wants advice. Carlo suddenly develops an intense fascination with a nearby postcard rack; I am forced to converse with a stranger. She tells me she's on holiday with her children and gestures to a large brood of assorted shapes and sizes sitting under a wide umbrella, eating ice cream. Her youngest child has got a foot full of sea urchin spines and she's wondering what to do. I feel a sharp, discordant grief that my children are not here; that we've left them in London with their very capable grandmother and dared to escape. Is it grief, or merely guilt? Is guilt a commodity I have acquired from the gods or does it make the very idea of gods redundant? Does it matter? Should I care? To respond to this woman and her child's needs, to say anything intelligent at all, requires a presence, a commitment from me which I would much rather dedicate right now to admiring the sun on my ever-darkening skin and the line of Carlo's jaw.

Sepia, the ink of the cuttlefish, has been used as a remedy since the earliest days of homeopathy. It was discovered by Samuel Hahnemann watching his male patient (an artist with failing health on whom Sam's medicine just wasn't working) sit at his easel and repeatedly lick his sepia-filled brush – thus giving birth not only to a major player in the homeopathic materia medica but to the concept of the maintaining cause.

With this provenance, it's curious that Sepia has since evolved, metamorphosed even, into a remedy used primarily by women.

The female cuttlefish, though prized in death as a source of food, is notorious in life for one bad thing. She is a very neglectful mother. Whereas the octopus, from the same family of cephalopods, actively dies in the process of hatching her young by choosing to starve rather than stop incubating, the cuttlefish, who abandons her eggs as soon as they are laid, just doesn't seem to care.

This behaviour is reflected in the imbalances of women who, having experienced major hormonal events such as childbirth or menopause, or having been assaulted by major hormonal drugs such as the Pill, HRT or IVF treatments, shut down in some way and cease to function from a nurturing spirit. The cuttlefish squirts its ink at its predators to create a kind of smokescreen as it propels itself fast in the opposite direction. Similarly, the Sepia mother may produce an obfuscating emotional fog, particularly impenetrable to those closest to her – to her children and her man. There is a dislike of men in the Sepia state, alongside a masculinization process, provoked by the accumulation of androgens in the adrenal glands, which hardens the physique and produces facial hair. It has been said that this is in accord with the emotional withdrawal, a viewpoint within which festers the deeply insidious idea that to be emotionally absent is somehow the natural state of the human male. The path of sexual politics running from ancient Greece, where the lunar, female principle was already considered inferior to the solar male, through Hahnemann's day, by which time the repression of women was at its zenith to the present continuing struggle for women's rights, is a sinuous one. Something fishy lurks in our persistent interpretation of the role of women to be first and foremost the nurturers of the young. To lack maternal feeling is to be considered simply wrong.

As a homeopath, to prescribe Sepia is often to make a judgement based on an assumption that roles are fixed, not fluid. At least in ancient Greece, where Zeus gave birth to Athena from his forehead, and where homosexuality was invented, the roles, and the rules, fluctuated like waves in the amniotic sea.

The physiological reason for the beneficial action of the remedy, Sepia, on the female hormones is due to the effect of melanin, the main ingredient of cuttlefish ink, on the adrenal glands. In humans, an imbalance of melanin can go two ways.

Hypoadrenia, adrenal insufficiency, produces physical and mental apathy, a droopy, heavy stasis, a condition in which there is a vacuum of feeling, a state in which the talent for metamorphosis has failed.

Hyperadrenia, an over-stimulation of the adrenal glands, produces aggression, conflict and the desire to be separate from others. As the Sepia woman becomes more like a man, she adopts a posture of combat. She pursues a career at the expense of her home life. She prefers the linear male struggle of competing in the world to the challenge of the female energy, which is to be a deep, wide, open yet encompassing space. The dark shape of the sepia ink cloud, which forms a decoy self to confuse the enemy, recalls this space inasmuch as it is a ghost shadow, the body in the water that isn't really there.

I phone home, and get Grandma. Everything's fine. Ricky, the youngest, is missing me a bit – when he has time. The other two? Why should they? They're proto-adults, "Stomping around like royalty, as usual," my mother says.

I hang up and stretch out in the recliner with a pile of books.

Gutman writes of the 'intellectual indolence' of Sepia[3]. Gibson talks of 'the desire to escape.'[4] Ralph Twentyman describes how Apollo, the major god of healing, keeps himself slightly aloof, 'ordering from a distance,' whereas Dionysus, who brought healing into the world via the vine, 'plunges into the turmoil, the wild dance of reality, aiming not at calm but at ecstatic union with God.'[5]

As I close my eyes and drift into a different consciousness, aided by the hot sun and my own tumultuous dreams, I wonder briefly if I'm eating too much fish.

In the evening, after swimming, I sit in a rock pool, examining the water. While I investigate how far down I can see, how clearly I can pick out the shapes of stones, and as I try

3 William Gutman M.D – Homeopathy, The Fundamentals of its Philosophy, The Essence of Its Remedies: The Homeopathic Medical Publishers, Bombay, 1986

4 Dr Douglas Gibson – Studies Of Homeopathic Remedies: Beaconsfield, 1987

5 Ralph Twentyman – Medicine, Mythology & Spirituality: Sophia Books, The Rudolf Steiner Press, Forest Row, 2004

to count all the little darting creatures without squinting, I become aware of an old woman further along the beach, thrashing a cuttlefish on a rock. She is working with a fervour which seems to compete with, or maybe respond to, the cumulative heat of the day.

"What's she doing?" I ask Carlo. "Beating it into submission?"

"No, cara," he replies, "she's tenderising. She's making it tender."

As we watch her wield the flabby body in the fading light, bringing flesh to meet stone like centuries of women before her, I wonder just how far beyond myself I can go. Carlo wraps himself around my uncertainties with a kiss.

"Come." He takes my hand in his. "You have an appointment with me."

We walk along the shoreline under the darkening sky. Carlo points out a constellation or two, stars emerging into relief as the night draws us a map which the daylight never can. We stop for a moment to admire the moon on the water and listen to the music spilling from a nearby bar, and then we carry on – to the place where energy and matter undress each other's darkness, where cats dine out with kings, where gods expose their frailty, where bones are washed and washed again by the tide, where silence waits, where love treads stealthily – no footprint on the sand – where children push against the limits of the water, where the door to Olympus, the eye of the cuttlefish, opens, where heroes dream, where mothers weep, where Peleus and Thetis meet the sea.

The Fairest Of Us All

> *'But what have we to do, some will ask, with the intelligence of the bees? What concern is it of ours whether this be a little less or a little more? Why weigh, with such infinite care, a minute fragment of almost invisible matter, as though it were a fluid whereon depended the destiny of man?'*
>
> *Maeterlinck – The Life Of The Bee*

An organic farm, somewhere in the English countryside, location for the yearly Homeopaths' Camp.

There's a big, fat bee in the pavilion and it's freaking Jane out. Due to her high-level histamine response to anything with a sting, she is starting to buzz with anxiety. Michelle, our designated shamanic warrior priestess for the afternoon, is by contrast, but in a similarly animated fashion, alive with pleasure.

"The bee is a symbol of community." She beams at Jane in an all-knowing, Mother Goddess type way. "Let it rest with us in peacefulness."

I dig Jane in the ribs and offer her a discreetly rolled-up sheaf of shamanic A4 notepaper.

"What's that for?" she asks, turning to me with a mad look in her eye.

"To kill it," I suggest.

"You kill it," she suggests back – her mad eye now firmly fixed on the bee, which is grazing sweetly on the pavilion's grassy floor.

"But I like bees."

Michelle, having been sufficiently distracted by her own fabulousness to notice that we have yet to move on from the bee issue, is explaining about our primal connection to nature and our sacred responsibility, both individual and collective, towards the spiritual growth of all beings. She glides towards the altar in the middle of the circle, arms out-stretched.

"Earth! Fire! Air! Water!" she cries.

A voice behind me, belonging to one of the 5:30pm gin-crew, mutters something facetious about not forgetting the olives.

There is a sudden thwacking noise, a blur of movement and a cry of "I can't stand it!" as Jane jumps up from her chair, arms flailing, and rushes from the pavilion, the bee in hot pursuit.

Michelle now fixes her antennae firmly in my direction, frowning somewhat as she struggles to regain her thread. I imagine Jane running screaming down the field, a psychotic bee on her tail, and hope my guilt by association will be enough to spiritually connect the three of us for ever more.

Michelle sighs, then holds her arms aloft once again and, as the shamanic forces gather round her swelling bosom, I gather the scattered notepaper lying at my feet, blushing slightly and congratulating myself on coming back from an idyllic Greek island – for this.

Someone coughs, someone else starts to drum and, with a flutter of her vermillion-shadowed eyelids, Michelle intones the magic words.

"Let us begin."

Later, arriving back at our corner of the camp, thoroughly ready for a little snooze, I find the gin-crew in full swing.

Mary has procured ice-cubes from the café. Felix, for it was he, has purchased a large jar of olives from the farm shop and the Visiting Celebrity Homeopath has just arrived from Heathrow with a suitcase full of tequila and six limes. Jane is nowhere to be seen.

As I wonder whether to go and look for her or just trust that she's not lying behind a hedge somewhere in anaphylactic shock, Linda proposes a toast to the VCH. We raise our plastic picnic beakers.

"It's a bit like having royalty round, isn't it," Mary giggles. "Bit like the Queen dropping in."

The VCH is, in fact, wearing purple. I take a seat next to Dave, who has spent the past week inevitably being known as 'Camp David' and who now has his back to me, engaged in earnest discussion with Felix. The others are busy chatting about the impending lunar eclipse and the crop circle which appeared this morning in the next-door farmer's field. The alcohol combines with the fresh air in my lungs and the empty space in my stomach to produce warm waves of love in my heart for this company of mavericks, so different from the uptight urban homeopaths back home who have no idea how to party.

As I hold out my beaker for a refill, and more love, I feel the log on which Dave and I are sitting start to vibrate, and I realize he and Felix are arguing.

"No! It's called Colony Collapse Disorder, and it didn't just start in 2006 actually, but has been observed throughout history, so it can't be environmental. It's BIOTIC!"

Felix positively hisses the last word, and slams his fist on the table, almost sending the ice bucket into the VCH's lap.

"Bollocks," says Dave, pouring Her Majesty another large one and then emptying the bottle into his own beaker. "The numbers are clear. Just look at the time line. It's mobile phone masts. Get with the programme, Biotic-Man!"

"Colony Collapse Disorder? Sounds like us lot when the tequila's run out," Linda says, eyeing her empty beaker and Dave's full one.

As the VCH offers to fetch another bottle from her VIP suite at the far end of the field, and Mary volunteers to forage for more limes, Felix turns on Linda, spitting rage and olive pits.

"It's not funny! It's really, really not funny!"

"Oh, have another drink, Felix, why don't you. Oh, you can't, Dave's just helped himself to the lot," Linda counters, effortlessly delivering a double-whammy.

There is a poisonous tinge to the air, something swarming through the bonhomie.

"What's all the fuss about?" I enquire, hoping to defuse the situation with a little abject ignorance. "What's wrong?"

Dave squeezes the last remaining lime in existence into his tequila and then throws it at Felix, who starts to giggle. Linda's eyebrows converge.

"Haven't you heard?" she says. "They're disappearing and no-one knows why."

"What are?" I'm lost in a tequila-soaked, shamanic bubble of incomprehension.

"What are?" she mimics, "What are? Why, the bees, you silly. The bees."

Oh yeah... Jane.

I find her in the café, having just emerged from a long weeping session in the shower. She is refreshed, if a little damp.

"The VCH finally got here," I say, cheerfully.

"Wicked! Did Michelle notice I left?"

"Oh... doubt it. She was very, very, very busy."

"And how was it for you?" she asks, lighting a roll-up and taking a deep drag. "Did the earth move?"

I know she wants me to reassure her that she didn't miss much. And that no one talked about her after she left. But there is an elephant in the room, or rather the café, and in fact it's not an elephant – it's a bee. I let it hover.

"Well, I am, as you well know, very earthy yet, at the same time, very fiery, also very watery and I have dreams of flying which I guess makes me very airy, so, one could say, I suppose, that yes, all in all, I had a fully-rounded experience."

Jane looks at me as if she can't quite believe my pomposity.

"Let's eat," she says.

We manoeuvre our way through a clutch of hungry homeopaths towards the counter and the café gods, Rick and Sheila, who wait with pasta, hot chocolate and dessert.

"I was thinking," Jane says, her mad eye now safely locked on to a double helping of toffee pudding. "If I pretend not to be frightened, maybe the bee would just go away, leave me alone. Maybe I'm creating the situation by being so..."

"Self-important?" I proffer.

Jane licks her spoon, considers.

"There's a difference between self-importance and self-worth, isn't there?"

"Shall we suggest it as a discussion topic for tomorrow?" I say, sleepily, the pasta vying with the hot chocolate for supremacy of my stomach. "I'm sure it would go down well with Michelle."

The homeopathic remedy made from Apis Mellifica, the honeybee, is probably the most accessible, most easily understood homeopathic remedy of all.

Everyone knows what a bee sting looks like and if you're lucky enough to have never been stung yourself, you will undoubtedly know someone who has. Red, hot, swollen, stinging, bursting – you see, you know the keynotes already. So, yes, we can and do treat a bee sting with Apis but, following the principle of like curing like, any medical condition or allergic reaction that has these keynote characteristics may respond to this remedy. Heat, stinging pains and swelling of the tissues are common reactions to various allergens, as well as symptoms of many other acute conditions such as abscesses, cystitis or injury. Rheumatoid arthritis, and chronic diseases involving lung, liver, kidney or heart, typically have oedema, or swelling due to excess fluid, as part of their picture. The symptom match is more important than the name of the complaint. This is not just a remedy for a sting.

As Michelle so rightly pointed out, the bees are renowned for their communal lifestyle and commitment to the welfare of the whole community. They are hierarchical in a most pragmatic way, and always busy. Even when they look like they're asleep, or dead, they are performing vital functions within the hive. The wondrous skilfulness of bees, their extraordinary powers of navigation, feats of engineering and communication as well as their crucial role in the earth's ecosystem are all worth looking into. But not here.

In homeopathy, where we are concerned with the effects of the poison, the emphasis when deciding on the relevance of the bee's behaviour in making a bigger picture of the remedy, tends to focus on the one bee who, more than any other, demands our attention – the Queen.

In the patient needing Apis on a mental/emotional level, the major physical keynote of swelling finds a mirror in the swollen ego of one who considers herself to be more important than anyone else. Whether this is in fact the case or merely a delusion is immaterial – the idea is what matters. And mattering is what Apis does best.

Just as the Queen Bee will not tolerate any rival for her throne, the Apis patient becomes upset if she does not hold the centre of attention. However, the Queen Bee, as a true queen, need only lie back and receive from her subjects – her sole function being to swell until she is ready to give birth. By contrast, the Apis patient is jealous, hard to please, insistent on her regal status and may display a kind of vexatious anxiety similar to an angry worker bee that has been interrupted in her most important work. A tendency to become over-heated, both emotionally as well as physically, is characteristic of the picture. This can make life very uncomfortable for the patient and anyone they encounter.

The materia medicas all describe a state of 'joylessness' among the mental symptoms of Apis – a depression that has been brought about, I would imagine, by taking herself far too seriously.

10.a.m. Sunday morning, the climax of our week, and despite the excesses of the night before (the crazy Irish fiddle music we jigged to till the small hours; the crop-circle we just had to visit at dawn; the fitful, restless sleep we may or may not have managed to snatch) plus the fight for the showers we have endured once more and the run on Rick and Sheila's coffee reserves, we are present again in the pavilion.

Homeopaths, like all self-appointed experts, are tough to teach because we know everything already. However, as the VCH finally takes the floor and proceeds to wipe it with us, we cannot help but recognise we are indeed in the presence of genuine homeopathic royalty.

The tequila hangover is a clever touch, rendering all members of the gin-crew monosyllabic and therefore ensuring all obvious troublemakers are silenced.

Jane's mad eye is lurking quietly behind a pair of oversized dark glasses. Felix droops, his head resting on Dave's shoulder, which droops too. Linda has at least taken the top off her pen in an attempt to look professional but failed to actually write anything down so far, and Mary is perched by the entrance, holding the power cable for the computer in place with her Wellington boot. We may all look asleep, or even dead, and yet vital functions are being performed. If there are any pretenders to the throne present among the more sober elements of our hive, they're flying so far below the radar as to be of no consequence whatsoever.

And where's Michelle, I wonder, momentarily letting my mind wander off-message while the VCH nobly leads us through an exercise in comparative imponderables. I'm sure she was here a minute ago. I think she was sitting right next to me. She can't have just buzzed off. It's so... impolite.

I crane my neck to look round the large tent pole and out into the field beyond. I catch a glimpse of vermillion hovering at the far end. It's Michelle, packing.

The VCH pauses and looks at her watch.

"Elevenses?"

We nod vigorously as one and start to move en masse towards the cafe. Unruly as we are, the VCH has brought us admirably into line. I don't know at this point if I'm merely a worker or a queen-in-waiting but I move along with the rest of the swarm, hoping the coffee won't run out, hoping the bees will not disappear and wondering if it will rain before Jane and I get the tent down.

The Speed Of Dark

'As nightfall does not come all at once, neither does oppression. In both instances, there is a twilight when everything remains seemingly unchanged. And it is in such twilight that we must all be aware of changes in the air, however slight, lest we become unwitting victims of the darkness.'

William O. Douglas

I'm leaving the gig early. The violation of aesthetic distance, provoked by my working knowledge of the lead singer's gastric complaint, compels me towards the exit. One can only take so much.

It's never a good idea to mix business with pleasure in this way, but the lead singer, my patient, had been very persuasive. A benefit do for the family of a recently murdered teenager. Hard to refuse. Having coerced a few friends to come along, and having done my bit to swell the coffers, I'm now pretending to have a headache and going home alone. Amid accusations of being a party-pooper and other, less refined remarks, I get my coat.

Emerging through the double doors, held open by a mildly attractive and outrageously flirtatious bouncer, I wander down the road slightly out of focus and, quite frankly, more than a little chuffed by his parting innuendo, which has done much to redress the unpopularity I had so keenly felt a moment before.

Turning left towards where I think I parked my car, I find myself in an alley with no street lights. Where am I exactly? Somewhere between Bayswater and Notting Hill, that much I know. I stop, hesitate, confused. Suddenly, I am slammed against the wall and a man's face is staring into mine. He seems very angry, and is muttering unintelligibly. He has my arms pinned.

In rapid succession, I have these thoughts:

"He looks crazy"

"His breath stinks"

"Where did he come from?"

"I can't move my arms"

"I should have stayed at the gig"

"I'm actually TERRIFIED!"

"OH SHIT!"

However, thanks to several years of tai chi training, I manage to override all these thoughts but one, and bring my attention firmly into the physical present, to the fact that I'm unable to move my arms. I let them go limp, become soft and therefore less tangible, less easy to hold. I force myself to look into his eyes.

"Why do you want to hurt me?" I ask, quietly.

He stops muttering, stares hard at me, his fetid breath caught for a moment in the space between us. Then he releases my arms with an exclamation of deep disgust and runs off down the alley like a gangly ball of chaos, shouting in a language I don't recognize.

My knees start to buckle in a post-traumatic way. Should I crawl back to the gig? No, I can't. The bouncer might misinterpret my return, think I took his come-on seriously. God, that could be embarrassing. Hang on, am I really thinking about sex at a time like this? Is that insane or just deeply Freudian? Freud! Ugh! Help, I want my Mum! I have to get my bearings.

I walk quickly back the way I came and realize, as I reach the brightly lit road, that I'd previously turned left instead of right and, despite feeling nauseous and starting to cry, I find the car and quickly lock myself inside. It's okay. I'm safe.

I feel too rattled to just plunge homeward. I need some human contact right now. But I don't know anyone in West London anymore. Yes, I do. Erroll's brother, Marcus, has a drinking club round here somewhere. I dig my phone out of my pocket.

Marcus rolls up in minutes, like a knight in a black sedan.

"Follow me, babe. We're just around the corner."

Inside the club, I'm ushered to a table at the back. Looks like I'm the only white person here. Marcus puts a bottle of rum on the table. The click clack of the domino players soothes me for a few seconds but I think vomiting is not out of the question. I take a swig of rum as Early, Marcus's business partner, joins us.

"So," Early says, thoughtfully, "do you want us to get a posse together and go fetch this bastard? Break his legs?"

Marcus hasn't brushed his hair for 35 years and has dreadlocks down to his bottom. Early is all shiny suit and loafers and probably carries a gun.

"No, thanks." I try and look grateful. "He's long gone. Crazy guy."

"He probably just been kicked outta the nuthouse." Early looks at Marcus who nods, sagely. "You was unlucky, that's all."

"The thing is..." I put one word gingerly in front of another. I feel a rum-fuelled garrulousness coming on. "The thing is, about luck... the thing is... my two older children have both been mugged this year, Tina more than once. She says it's racially motivated. Tyrone says it's just percentages. I never think of myself as a target, I guess. This guy was mad, it's different I know, but what about the other stuff? I've just been to a gig in honour of a murdered teenager. Why do you need posses and why do you think violence is the response to violence?"

I don't actually say the last bit, stop myself in time. Early examines his trouser creases. He understands the unspoken.

"Black on black killin'? Government's secret weapon, innit, like cheap crack," he replies. "Teenagers killin' teenagers? One way to get rid of a lost generation."

"Everyone is born with the weight of death on their shoulders," Marcus says softly, shaking nuts into a bowl and offering me some.

"Do you feel the weight of any responsibility, though?" My thoughts are dangerously borderline now. No more scrapes tonight, please, verbal or otherwise, the diplomat who resides somewhere deep within me requests. I press on, regardless. "Do you feel that you, as grown up, conscious black men, might have something to do with it, with how we got to this... this darkness?"

Early stiffens slightly, adjusts his cuffs and leans towards me with an exasperated, almost intimidating gaze.

"Why, are you writin' a book?"

Propelled by the weight of my own ineptitude, I rock backwards in my chair.

"Funny you should mention it, yes I am. Taking notes, anyway."

Marcus smiles beatifically. Early roars with laughter and slaps his be-ringed hand hard on my thigh.

"Then tell you what..." He stops to regard the consequence of his gesture which, for a moment, causes my chair to teeter even further back before righting itself with a dull thud that I feel all the way up my spine. Then he picks up the bottle of rum and waves it at me. "Tell you what. Why don't you kiss my ass and we'll make it a love story."

In homeopathy we have several substances which address the needs of the Victim. But, straightforward it ain't. The rubric: 'Ailments from being abused' contains 44 remedies, which is quite a lot of variations on a theme. In addition, the patient, whether sick in mind or body, will more than likely be feeling victimized anyway, just by virtue of being ill. To complicate things further, according to the Karpman Drama Triangle,[6] which extrapolates the archetypal fairytale plotline of damsel in distress, wicked ogre and prince on a white charger and applies it to everyday human relationships, for every Victim there is a Persecutor and a Rescuer.

If the patient presents as a Victim, and the Persecutor is an external influence of some kind, the practitioner's task is always to avoid being set up as the Rescuer. Why? Because the triangle is active, it moves and shifts and, therefore, a Rescuer will inevitably have to move at some point in the relationship to the position of Victim or Persecutor. By succumbing to the seductive invitation to rescue, the homeopath may find herself enmeshed in a power play which cannot, in the end, produce a therapeutic result.

However, returning to the random mugging and senseless killing of children by children which blight our lives, there

6 A model developed by Dr Stephen Karpman from Transactional Analysis. Most novels, plays and movies depend on this plot structure. Widely used in therapeutic circles to understand dysfunctional relationships.

are two homeopathic remedies which may help to address this development in our culture, remedies which shine clearly in the darkness – Staphysagria, the delphinium, and Anacardium Orientale, the marking nut. I lie awake often, fantasizing about how to put these two in the local water supply without getting caught but never progress too far with my plan as, despite the obvious practical, legal and ethical ramifications of such a move, I am undecided as to whether it would be a bold act of counter-terrorism on my part or a Rescuer tendency gone mad.

Staphysagria is a remedy for the effects of invasion of personal space. We homeopaths usually think of it first when confronted in the consulting room with yet another tale of abuse, trauma, attack, medical mistreatment or other offence visited upon the patient. As these stories reveal themselves, it may become apparent that the residue of the invasion has caused the patient to adopt an attitude of meekness which covers up a huge amount of suppressed anger and humiliation. This is in order to avoid further abuse – a strategy that, unfortunately, often fails.

Repeated humiliation or abuse may compound the suppression and lead to physical symptoms as the body tries to cope with what the mind cannot. It is usually at this point that the homeopath comes in.

The poisonous seeds of the delphinium have a marked effect on the nervous system, with initial irritation and hypersensitivity in various parts of the body leading to paralysis and death by asphyxiation. This is mirrored in the state of agitated humiliation and indignation which the Staphysagria patient also produces but doesn't express, leading to a kind of asphyxiation of the personality.

There is a marked effect on the alimentary and genito-urinary systems, with irritation made worse from the slightest touch. Staphysagria is known both as 'the mother-in-law remedy' and as a cure for 'honeymoon cystitis', thereby indicating a dubious link between sexual activity, (consensual or otherwise), marriage and victimization.

The teeth are particularly affected, decay and blackening being common, which causes a lack of 'bite' that again echoes the sense of powerlessness the Staphysagria patient feels.

However, it is also used as a remedy for head-lice and other parasites and is given after surgery to prevent adhesions, thereby demonstrating the gloriously impartial nature of homeopathy. The details have less relevance than the clear aetiology of invasion.

Anacardium is indicated when, as in the Karpman triangle, the Victim becomes the Persecutor; when the strategy for dealing with an abusive situation is to become cruel and visit abuse on others. Looking at the personal history of some of the great persecutors of our times, such as Hitler or Saddam Hussein, one finds a background of parental brutality and abuse which leads to the conclusion that gross cruelty is learned behaviour. One does not become an abuser without first having been abused or a tyrant without first having been tyrannized. I'm not suggesting this as a blanket rule but people who have been raised lovingly, and who have had their needs met in childhood, generally speaking, do not kill.

Anacardium is known as the marking nut because the milky yet corrosive juice between the shell and the kernel quickly blackens on exposure to air, and is traditionally used as a fabric dye. In a physical dose it will indeed mark the skin, causing blisters, redness and burning. It also affects the muscles, joints, nerves and the digestive system as well as having a profound effect on the mind. The remedy is produced from this juice and contains a metaphor in the liquid darkening that guides us to its use.

Now, sitting in the club, nursing a wounded sense of complacency and an awkward desire to disrupt the complacency of others, what I really need in order to recover my equilibrium, to reclaim my invaded space, is a large dose of Staphysagria. Instead, I get Early, who may well be asking, in his most civilized yet disturbingly aggressive way, for a dose of Anacardium. Time to go.

So he clicks his fingers at Marcus, who is already behind the bar looking for a snack for me to have on my way home; hands me his card, on which I read his name is actually Hurley; ushers me into a waiting cab and tells me not to worry about the fare as the driver's on the payroll.

Crossing the Thames, having decided not to even think about the need to return tomorrow morning to get my car, I start to question everything. Have I just been rescued or did I rescue myself? Did the mad guy with the bad breath see me as a persecutor rather than a victim? Does Early rescue by persecution? Was I trying to goad Early into something persecutory or were we both clear that we could be victims if we chose but we prefer not? Are he and Marcus victims of racist stereotyping? Did I pick up some stray victim ectoplasm at the gig? Why do I never expect to be mugged yet my children expect it on a daily basis? If we are to stop being 'unwitting victims of the darkness' and prevent further killings, whom must we persecute, or prosecute? Whom should we rescue? Was I 'Asking for it?'

I open my handbag and gaze despairingly at its contents, while feeling an urgent need to shove all my unanswered questions into its darkness and zip it up. There is a roadblock up ahead. My driver, Quincy, says it looks like an accident, or maybe an incident.

I burrow down into the depths of his upholstery, just wishing to be back home with my loved ones, just hoping they're okay.

As Quincy slows down in order to take a diversionary route, I look at my watch. 4:30 a.m. Dawn soon, dawn on the river. The darkness is lifting for another day.

Organization

I call in at the printers' collective where I worked when I first came to London. Kieran, a founder member who lives upstairs from the presses, has just come out of hospital and I've done his shopping for him. As he is a devout unbeliever in homeopathy, it's the best I can do. Kieran has been seriously ill and is in a state of dazed euphoria, partly because he's still alive and getting better, and partly because he's medicated up to the eyeballs. I resist scrutinizing the mess of pill bottles by his chair. His antipathy towards all complementary medicine stems mainly from his hard-left leanings and devotion to the NHS, which should, in his view, have no rivals. Although I have pointed out to him on several occasions that I spend part of my working life delivering free treatments to the unwaged through a publicly funded agency, he still considers me, if not a complete class traitor, at least a bit of a sell-out. No matter. We both know we want to make the world a better place. The rest is just detail.

Pausing in the loo, I shudder at the archeology of stains in the toilet bowl and yearn to give the whole place a good scrub. But I must also resist offering to get my rubber gloves on, as this is how Kieran likes it. For as long as I've known him he's nested comfortably in his own detritus, a quality which I admire for its refusal to conform to our germ-fearing culture and, simultaneously, abhor because the place is a festering tip.

We drink strong tea out of chipped mugs and he fills me in on the latest political scandals that have beset the collective since my last visit some months ago, and in which he has a starring role. As he weaves the different strands together, and I get used to the long pauses between sentences, I picture a web of intrigue, taut with poison, surrounding my old workplace. I remember, without a trace of nostalgia, the hours of mind-crushing boredom spent in endless meetings during which people went on and on and on about the most tedious aspects of communal enterprise, with often a smattering of Marxist rhetoric thrown in for light relief, but which we all knew had to be endured to keep the place functioning cohesively.

Now, it seems, decisions are being taken in secret, deals have been brokered without due process, consultation has left the building and the black-hearted power-seekers are on the rise. My web metaphor gets tangled up in my mind with Kieran's invocation of Machiavelli and The Borgias and, as I wonder whether I'm getting a contact high from his medication, I suggest to him that the controversy is like a giant spider from 15th century Italy which has turned on itself by way of gnawing off its own limbs and that the struggle for domination of the oxygen supply is being won by a kind of perverted, self-loathing parasite eating its way through from the inside.

"Exactly," says Kieran,"and it's coming my way."

Once, in order to get rid of a disagreeable patient, I looked her in the eyes and told her I was going to give her arsenic. She never came back. As a 'suspicion of medicines' is a key-note of the Arsenicum type, it was a calculated move. You may be shocked to learn that a homeopath would consider tactics of this sort, or that to dislike a patient is even a possibility. We are, in fact, trained to view the arrival of the disagreeable as hugely positive in the sense that it provides an opportunity for our inner growth, embodying aspects of our own, but un-owned, Shadow. This is tough work, and I guess I must just have been having a bad day. And, anyway, it was true. She needed arsenic for her asthma.

If you haven't yet come to grips with the homeopathic principle of like curing like, you may be even more shocked to learn that arsenic is one of the most important remedies in the medicine chest. Administered in small quantities over time, the disorganizing effect of arsenic poisoning will produce skin and digestive symptoms, followed by damage to heart, lungs, blood and nervous system. Consequently, given this wide-ranging action, it has a curative effect homeopathically in many conditions, from the banal to the life-threatening.

Famed in ancient Rome as a discreet way to dispatch one's enemies, arsenic reappeared at the forefront of the poisoner's repertoire during the Renaissance. Indeed, the Borgias used arsenic to get rid of several disagreeable people and a suspicion of medicines would have been considered prudent in the days of the euphemistically entitled 'Inheritance Potions'. An odourless, tasteless and transparent substance, arsenic could be conveniently administered without detection so that a slow, mysterious death was as common as one that was nasty, brutish and short.

It is rumoured that Napoleon suffered arsenic poisoning from inhaling the copper arsenate emanating from a pigment known as Scheele's Green that covered the damp walls of his house in St. Helena. To think Napoleon may have been murdered by his wallpaper brings me to the theme developing here as I sit on Kieran's grotty sofa, contemplating the machinations of his enemies and his current exile whilst inhaling whispers of old rubbish and printer's ink. Where better to see Arsenicum display its greed-for-power pathology than in the battle for control of the organization? While Kieran and I talk of Marx, I remember Groucho, who once said, 'I have a mind to join a club and beat you over the head with it.'

The mental keynotes of Arsenicum Album, the white oxide that is the most commonly used form of the remedy, are anxiety, restlessness, desire for company and an abhorrence of germs. The impetus which seemingly drives these activities is a fear of loss of control. However, underlying this issue is a greater fear and the selfishness and greed Arsenicum also displays is caused by a constant questioning of their own ability to survive. The suspicion of medicines goes hand in hand with a profound fear of death. To keep this threat at bay, Arsenicum will become dictatorial and highly critical, issuing commands and complaining bitterly if they are not executed just so. As Catherine Coulter observes in her essay on Arsenicum, 'the tongue is the one organ that retains its full powers throughout even the most severe illness.'[7] The mental and physical restlessness create a need for organization and cleanliness that can become obsessive as the underlying fear of disintegration propels the Arsenicum patient to impose order on the external world. "Licking the skirting board," as Kieran puts it.

So, a remedy for divas, control freaks and anal-retentives. In the light of this, you may have another shock coming

7 Catherine R. Coulter-Portraits of Homeopathic Medicine: Vol. 1. Ninth House Publishing, 2002

the first time your homeopath prescribes Arsenicum for you. What can she mean?

It was not unusual for me to tell my disagreeable patient the name of the remedy. Aware that my position as a transient authority figure in any of my patients lives is always open to abuse on my part, I tend to err on the side of too much information in an attempt to give back to the patient the power which they feel has been eroded by illness and lofty over-management by the allopathic medical brigade. This is in contrast to many homeopaths, who withhold the name of the remedy in case the substance it is made from sounds too gruesome, or the patient looks it up in a book and decides not to take it. This indicates a lack of trust on the homeopath's part, I feel – trust in the patient, the healing process, the remedy and, most worryingly, in her own credibility – and a desire for control which one could file under Arsenicum without too great an imaginative leap. The natural desire for a good outcome of treatment can get caught in the web of the homeopath's need to prove herself. Position, reputation, job-satisfaction and bank-balance are all precariously linked to results. To prevent outcome getting tangled up with income it is necessary to relinquish attachment to one's desire to win, however much the feeding of one's young depends on it. To quote Hahnemann, 'The mentioning of Arsenic calls up powerful recollections in my soul,'[8] and it is this remedy, more than any other, that strikes at the core of the homeopath's integrity. Survival issues run deep in us all.

Of course, in the case of the stereotypical Arsenicum patient, it *is* likely that, having turned up in an impeccably

8 Samuel Hahnemann – Chronic Diseases: Vol. 5. W.M.Radde, New York, 1839

coordinated outfit; raised an eyebrow at the books scattered on the consulting-room floor and pointedly smoothed the creases from the sofa cushions before sitting down; interrogated me as to my qualifications and fitness for the job; described the dark world they currently inhabit as being full of enemies, possibly medical, conjugal, professional; decreed that their asthma/migraine/insomnia/gastro-enteritis/sciatica will prove the most challenging and fascinating case I have ever taken and therefore probably impossible to cure, (I make a point to nod enthusiastically in agreement at this, as if I can't imagine where to even begin); produced a neatly bound sheaf of notes in beautifully executed cursive script, detailing the precise time, consistency and odour of their bowel movements or, even worse, handed me a photocopy so we can read through them together, they will find the news that they're going to be given arsenic, unlike the remedy itself, hard to swallow. This is where a little skill is required, and a knowledge of politics is useful.

The temptation to control the process by controlling the patient must be subservient to the principles of the collective. By the time the point of naming the remedy has arrived, the presumption of a common goal must have become a reality in the room. When this point has been reached, even those needing Arsenicum will have no qualms. My disagreeable patient could have been wooed into accepting the prescription if I had handled it differently, if I had felt differently. My desire to be rid of her flags up nothing more than my desire to be rid of some disagreeable part of myself.

I'm done lolling on the sofa with Kieran. He's hungry, so I quickly make some food for him and, searching for a plastic bag in which to confine the overflow of garbage in the kitchen, find a large, fat spider lurking behind the bin.

"You know what, K," I say, returning to the sitting room, "things could be worse. At least you're not being bugged."

"True," he says, wearily, "but I am being followed."

"Given that you haven't been downstairs in 3 weeks..."

"What I mean is, I was... before I got sick... I think they even spied on me in hospital, though that may have just been the morphine... Good job I'm ill, really. Puts things on... hold."

"Quite so," I say, doubtfully, concerned that I can only spectate – yet resolved to remain on the periphery of something that, apparently, is none of my business.

"However... as I'm hacking into their emails, I'm still one step ahead of the bastards... even in my pyjamas."

He smiles slowly, looking down at the bowl of soup I have put on the table in front of him.

"Go on," I say, "it's not poisoned."

"Ha!" He flexes a wasted bicep, then picks up the spoon I have placed next to the bowl, rubs it a few times on his trouser-leg, and admires himself in its reflective curve.

"Handsome chap," he murmurs.

"A prince," I concur.

He looks up at me with his half-closed eyes, dreamy and somehow warm and safe in his refusal to be conquered.

"I'm going now, K," I say. "Got to check in with the family."

Driving home, I realize that I've forgotten to take the rubbish that I'd bagged up and meant to throw into the nearest bin. Ah, well. As we are always telling our patients, random palliatives often lead to defective elimination, and it is better to do nothing than get it wrong. Perhaps I could bring him a paper-shredder next time, one of those manual ones, with a handle, beloved of hamster-owners and secretive small boys. Give his biceps something to do while he waits for his head to clear.

Wrapped in these thoughts, I stall at the lights and a disagreeable looking man in a 4x4 beeps me from behind. As I get back in gear, I notice he's actually driving something called a Land Rover Defender. Probably not a bad idea in Hackney. He overtakes and, in passing, throws me an ugly scowl through his open window, as if I have conspired to ruin his day.

"You may be king of the road for now, pal," I mutter, "but your warranty has an expiry date, just like everything else."

This sliver of anger, sharp and sudden as a dagger, reminds me of Tina's recent observation that, as far as I'm concerned, every other motorist in London seems to be called Dickhead.

Finding myself on the wrong side of the looking-glass world yet again, I accelerate through the trail of murky, poisonous exhaust from Defender Man's gleaming rear and turn to the left – a direction that feels more like home.

The Unprejudiced Observer

We've discovered that one of the cats is deaf – Violet, the champion climber. Unlike her brother, Cosmo, who's the nervous type, Violet has impressed the whole family since her arrival with her cavalier attitude to life and its obstacles. Curiously, the human being seems to be for her an obstacle of a particularly irritating kind and she avoids our proffered embraces with slinky disdain. Cosmo, on the other hand, has a tendency to flop all at once onto any vacant lap, needy and trembling with desire. Violet sleeps under things, out of reach. Cosmo snuggles in close. Violet doesn't avoid Cosmo's touch though. Often they curl up together, their limbs entwined.

When they first arrived they were too small to manage the wooden stairs which run like an aorta through the centre of the house and had to be carried from floor to floor. Violet was having none of this and it seemed to take her only minutes to master the art of stair-jumping, despite being the shorter-legged of the two. She then began to explore every surface on both horizontal and vertical planes and, like Ricky before her, to negotiate the inaccessible with the ease of a true climber. Ricky, needless to say, was ecstatic.

Her boldness now extends to pitching into the air, with one swipe of an adorable paw, any object she encounters en route. The mantle-piece and windowsills have had to be cleared and, though I have never really been one for ornaments, my lack of attachment to various fragile trinkets has been severely challenged by the recurring sound of something smashing on the floor. As I hoover up the remains of the latest casualty, Violet sits and watches unmoved for, after all, it is nothing to do with her.

Violet's dislike of physical contact doesn't stop her being present when there are people around or a job to be done. She's an interactive cat. While Cosmo quakes behind the curtains at the sound of the doorbell, Violet has had to be pulled miaowing from Brian, the window-cleaner's, soapy pail and disgorged from under the cooker during a visit from the Siemans engineer. She's run up and down the chimney several times, depositing soot everywhere. She likes the inside of the washing-machine and the top of the curtain rail. Her unruly bravery keeps me busy as she maps out a world of impossible games.

Outside, Violet travels over walls and up trees. Accessing the roof of the pergola with a few bounds, she seemingly walks on air, at one with the squirrels and a danger to birds. But she has yet to distinguish between garden – good climbing, and house – bad climbing. My vocal admonishments do nothing to intimidate her and when I lose patience and deposit her, squealing, outside the back door she returns immediately, as if what just happened didn't, and then wanders off to toy perhaps with a mobile phone or some other valuable left precariously unattended on a bookshelf.

One morning last week, I clattered loudly into the kitchen to make tea. Violet, perched on the table with her back to me, did a double-take as I walked past her to the kettle. A thought pierced my bleary somnambulism – she didn't hear me coming.

A few days later, as we sat on the back steps enjoying the sun, companionably together yet a respectful distance apart, a large vehicle shuddered to an ear-splitting halt in the street on the other side of the garden wall. Violet did not move so much as a whisker. I phoned the vet.

Mike not only has film-star looks but a way with animals which could bring sentimental tears to my eyes were it not for his annoying habit of trying to bait me with medical certainties whenever we meet. In the past our locking of horns has caused nervous veterinary assistants to give me and my creatures the widest of berths as I became what every practice dreads – the troublesome client. Eventually, I wised up and now agree at all times with everything he says, however inflammatory or ridiculous, resolving to concentrate instead on his many gifts, and whichever animal is currently on his examining table. Ideological battles have their place but, as with the GP, if I need a diagnosis I come for just that and take care of the medicines myself.

In return, Mike has stopped trying to impress me with his arsenal of expensive drugs and has conceded that nothing living of mine has yet died from homeopathy.

Violet melts under Mike's touch, submitting to his investigation of her ears with just a hint of coquettishness. Having found no sign of infection or scarring, he suggests performing the ultimate cat-hearing test.

"You get behind them and clap your hands and see if their ears twitch."

"Sounds good. Do you want to do it, or shall I?"

Mike waves me out of the way with a rank-pulling smile.

"Stand back," he says with quiet authority, "I've done this before."

He moves around the table so that Violet can't see him, and claps loudly. Nothing. He does it again, even louder.

Still nothing. He looks at me, his handsome brow wrinkling with concern.

"She's deaf. You must never let her outside again."

He proceeds to tell me about the notorious ginger tom of Bromley, deaf as a post, who has caused umpteen near collisions due to his habit of sitting in the middle of the one way system, facing away from the oncoming traffic and not stirring as juggernauts and other large vehicles slam on the brakes inches from his oblivious hind quarters.

I listen with just the one ear as I try to mentally process the entire canon of Violet's behavioural tics from this disturbingly new perspective and wonder how I could have been so dense – the recent braking of a large vehicle having, thankfully, been a catalyst for enlightenment. Mike regains my full attention by remarking that Violet has an unusually small head.

"Probably not much brain,"he says, cheerfully.

Home again, I prepare dinner, berating myself for my lack of observational skills and meandering down a morose alleyway called You are an inadequate cat-owner, a useless homeopath, a terrible mother and just stupid generally. Enumerating my shortcomings soon becomes boring, however, so I try and think constructively for a bit. I run through the list of Violet's habits again in the context of her deafness. Everything I had previously observed, witnessed, experienced, is now standing on its head. Her own very small head (oh yes, it is, isn't it, now you mention it) indicates a birth defect. Deaf since the beginning? If she can't hear the sound of breaking glass, or me shouting, if she's never heard at all, she's missing a huge amount of feedback regarding cause and effect. No wonder there are things she doesn't seem to learn. No wonder she took an age to stop peeing on The Guardian.

What does the exclusion of sound mean for a cat? Is that why she doesn't seem to be scared of anything? Of course – doesn't react to the hoover. Should have been obvious. It's not bravery but a lack of awareness. There was me thinking Violet was a reckless insouciant when in fact she's disabled. I'm still having difficulty adjusting. Is she autistic too, maybe? Is that why she doesn't like to be touched? I recall sensing an almost hypnotic quality to certain aspects of her behaviour as if she was stuck in some kind of repetitive loop. I didn't pursue the thought.

The more I do think, the more I dread telling Ricky the news. He identifies with Violet as a fellow free spirit, He loves her passionately. Violet's willfulness often reminds me of Ricky's. They become coupled in my mind sometimes. That'll have to change.

At least her balance doesn't seem to be affected.

And what of Cosmo, who is possibly having to do the hearing for two? Certainly puts a new spin on his behaviour. In order to survive, does Violet need to learn fear?

"You must never let her outside again." Yeah, right.

Testing the pasta for doneness, I don't notice the boiling water nestling in its curlicues and burn my lip. As I watch in the mirror over the sink, a swelling forms in seconds making me look as if I've been punched in the mouth. I smear Nelsons Burn ointment on it, which lessens the pain slightly, and wonder just how this will look in the morning.

Tina marches in, demanding to know when dinner will be ready as she's got an extra rehearsal at eight. Seeing my disfigurement she softens and, when I tell her the news about Violet, suggests I talk to Ricky sooner rather than later.

"Let the cat out of the bag, you mean?"

"No, I was thinking more put the cat among the pigeons. Look, Mum, don't make such a big deal. He'll probably like it."

"You don't remember when your favourite toy got broken, do you?"

"Violet's not a toy and she's not broken, she's just changed. And, if you remember, which you obviously don't, I never really saw the point of toys."

Tyrone slouches in, wearing headphones, and mimes hunger by pointing his finger to his empty mouth. I glare at him and purse my swollen lip, but he doesn't notice.

Tina and I watch as he carves a huge hunk of bread and smothers it in butter. Then he leaves, hips swaying and head bobbing to a rhythm neither of us can hear. Tina turns and follows him out, aping his loose-limbed shuffle by wiggling her pelvis, nodding exaggeratedly and putting her hands over her ears. I drain the pasta, and stand for a moment in a cloud of steam.

Next day I wake thinking of Ben Goldacre, as the remnant of a mildly erotic dream encounter between us shrivels with the dawn. I had fallen asleep reading his anti-homeopathy polemic in Bad Science.[9] A leading light in the campaign against homeopathy in the U.K., Ben writes with wit, vigour and, above all, the certainty that he is right. He has observed that homeopathy is an imprecise science which does not fit comfortably in a mechanistic, reductionist framework composed of straight lines and sharp angles

9 Bad Science, the book, not the Guardian column. Fourth Estate, 2009

and has concluded from this that it must, therefore, be nonsense, that all homeopaths are charlatans and that their patients are deluded fools.

The mugshot on the inside back cover does not do Ben justice. I know this because I once found myself at a rather dry debate on the efficacy of homeopathy hosted by the Science Museum, in which Ben presented the case for the opposition. Ben is tall, good-looking, boyishly charming. Being close to his aura of myth-busting, slim-hipped coolness, I understood why he is a hero to many and, in contrast to the balding middle-aged male homeopath appearing for our side, unspeakably glamorous.

The cleverness of Ben's book lies in his apparent impartiality. Having been accused, in the past, of being an apologist for Big Pharma due to his links with the Institute of Psychiatry, which partly relies on drug company money for its research funding, he lays into certain aspects of the industry with the same crusading zeal that he directs towards homeopathy – willing me to believe in him as a beacon of Scientific Truth. This is confusing, and the thought of having to read on makes me feel tired even though I've just woken up.

I've managed to placate Mike the vet's outraged objections to homeopathy by, well, basically ignoring him. To do the same to Ben may be a little harder. Read a book while simultaneously ignoring it? Gives the concept of Brain Gym[10] a whole new meaning.

Oh, Ben, if only things were different. If only my homeopathic mysteries could turn you on as much as a double-blind random placebo clinical control trial seems to do. What sweet music we could make together, healing

10 Bad Science – Chapter 2, for Ben's evaluation.

the world and ridding it of false positives and confounded variables along the way.

Violet jumps on the bed, squeaking at me. She wants something. Violet talks to me a lot. I used to answer, but now...

"Stop searching for a common language for you and Ben and start looking for one for you and Violet," I tell myself.

My lip hurts. Sure enough, it's even more purple and swollen, looking uncommonly like I've been in a fight. Will today's patients believe the pasta story or will they wonder with varying degrees of concern what kind of secret life their homeopath may be leading?

Ricky arrives for his morning cuddle. I still haven't said anything to him because he was tired and cranky last night, but it's top of my list.

He chases Violet off the bed and tries to get underneath it with her, but he's already too big. I suppose having a congenitally deaf and brain-damaged cat will be like having an eternal toddler around the place. That'll be nice.

"I took Violet to the vet yesterday," I say. "Her ears aren't working properly. She can't hear."

"What, you mean, like deaf?" Ricky replies.

"Yes, deaf."

"Oh," he says, "is that why when I make lots of noise, she still likes me?"

"Yes."

"Cool." He manages to drag her by the scruff of the neck from under the bed and folds her in his arms. She tries to wriggle from his grasp but he holds on – a little too tight.

"Hello, my deaf cat." He strokes her ears, then bellows loudly, "HELLO!"

"I think she's a hungry cat right now. Do you want to put her down and get her some breakfast?"

He drops Violet unceremoniously and leaps after her down the stairs.

Observation is a pillar of any medical discipline and in homeopathy, where we are encouraged to seek the unusual as a key to prescribing, we must always be wary of how we interpret the facts. That things are not what they seem is, paradoxically, a fact which we encounter often in the sense that whatever it is the patient ostensibly wants treating, the presenting complaint, is not necessarily what needs to be cured. However, before we filter, there is a state of neutrality in which we can simply observe. Hahnemann coined the term 'The Unprejudiced Observer' to describe this ideal state of receptive unknowing which must be the constant by which information is assessed. Actually, I just made that up. What he was referring to is the importance of only being interested in the symptomatic changes to the patient's usually healthy state, and not 'construct...empty speculations' concerning the patient's 'invisible interior'.[11] But, if you are reading this in a pro-homeopathy frame of mind, you'll probably believe whatever I write. It's a dilemma.

We may aspire to be free of prejudice but culture and values create judgment. To hold any belief at all is to simultaneously disbelieve something else. To hold that something is true, another thing must be untrue. We take up positions. The closest I can get to solving this intellectually is to entertain the possibility that there is always more

11 Samuel Hahnemann: Organon Of Medicine, 6th Edition. 1842

than one right answer to every question. "Are you sure?" is a question I ask myself daily, about all sorts of things.

Scientifically, in quantum theory there is something called the 'observer effect.' This refers to changes that the act of observation will always make on whatever is being observed. In other words, it is no longer acceptable to consider human consciousness as being separate from the physical world. Hahnemann developed his manifesto without the benefit of the discoveries of quantum physics but in formulating his method of high dilutions, which is the aspect of homeopathy that so enrages Ben and others, he appears to have been in tune with the sub-atomic world a mere two centuries earlier than anyone else.

The treatment of animals relies almost exclusively on observation, both by the practitioner and those who know the patient best. The efficacy of homeopathy in veterinary medicine is the proof we need that the remedies are not placebo. Ben tries to wriggle out of this one in his book, unsuccessfully I feel.[12] Positive results in the treatment of large numbers of farm animals are an uncomfortable spur on the hide of Ben's denial.

Thanks to my father, at whose knee I learnt the art of rebellion, I understand scepticism, and the urge to de-bunk. Thanks to homeopathy, which I learnt by trial and error of a different kind to that promulgated by the statisticians, I understand that if one is to be a sceptic one must also be sceptical of one's scepticism. After all, it's only fair.

Ben's argument is stale; his paradigm is curling at the edges. Curiously, of all the villains who populate his book, his main bête noire seems to be the media (without whom Ben would be just another anonymous NHS doctor), par-

12 Bad Science; p.79

ticularly newspapers that, according to Ben, have given far too much favourable coverage to alternative medicine and therefore an undeserved popularity and false credence to a bunch of lunatics such as myself. Let's not be sheepish – the real subject here is market competitiveness. As, when we talk of the War On Terror, we are really discussing oil, when we talk of homeopathy and other complementary therapies versus allopathic medicine, aren't we are really discussing drugs and profit? And even if Ben could convince me that his possible connections to the pharmaceutical industry play no part in his observations[13], I would still have to notice that he has an attachment to a pre-determined theoretical framework that blinds him to anything that doesn't fit. A line from Hamlet about there being more things in heaven and earth, Ben, than are dreamt of in your philosophy comes to mind.

I throw the book into the air and watch it fall. I've got more important things to do. The phrase 'don't bite the hand that feeds you' follows swiftly on, as I follow Ricky and Violet downstairs for breakfast.

13 I await his forthcoming book, 'Bad Pharma', with interest.

The Speed Of Dark 2: The Road To Hell

Saturday 1 a.m., the phone rings. My private line. A man's voice requests I confirm my identity. As my blood runs cold, I ask him why he wants to know. He says he's the desk sergeant at a central London police station and would I confirm I'm me because otherwise he can't tell me why he wants to know.

Stumbling out of bed, phone in hand, I do a quick tour of the house and a reassuringly complete head count, all fast asleep. While I nearly fall down the stairs in the dark, I'm informed that Jasper has been arrested for being drunk and disorderly. No charges have been brought yet but he's in a cell and there's a small matter of a packet of white tablets found on his person.

"He gave me your number. Says they're for his hay fever."

Panic gives way to fury. "You fool!" I want to blurt, "It's the middle of the bloody night!" Then relief becomes concern – concern for Jasper, and concern that there's a drug dealing implication nestling within this conversation. I deliver a snap-out-of-it-wide-awake account of my professional relationship to the detainee, and conclude by saying, "... so if you can be bothered to have them analysed, I guarantee you will find nothing in them."

The sergeant is not impressed. He hands me over to a volunteer from Advocacy In Mind, who tells me that Jasper was raving a bit before he passed out.

"I know this may sound weird, but are you his mother?"

"No, I'm his homeopath," I reply, and then have to go through the whole thing again. We agree to meet at the police station at 10:30 a.m. I hang up and try to go back to sleep.

My last patient of the day had been a little girl called Yasmin. It was her first visit. She had travelled across London on a Friday after school, accompanied by her mother, who insisted on doing all the talking while Yasmin chewed her hair and said nothing. I was told about Yasmin's difficulties with her sister, her 'bad' behaviour, her mood swings, her constant whining and her clinginess. It was uncomfortable, what with Yasmin being right there, listening. I needed to shut the mother up so I went for Plan B, (Plan A – suggesting the parent waits in another room while the child and I talk was just not going to happen.)

I opened a book of flower pictures and asked Yasmin to choose the ones she liked best. The mother moved closer and pointed out the one she thought was the prettiest. Yasmin shyly singled out her mother's favourite flower.

Plan C involves asking questions to which only the child knows the answer. I asked Yasmin if she remembered her dreams. She looked at the floor, her fingers twining her hair into tight little knots, then nodded briefly and, as her mother started to join in, I interrupted by asking Yasmin if there was anything she dreamt about regularly. Head still bowed, she nodded again but said nothing.

Usually, I would wait at this point but the mother, pouting slightly by now, needed to be contained.

"Can you tell me what that might be?" I asked as gently as possible, willing the mother to stay quiet and let her child speak. The air felt heavy, as if a lifetime's frustrations had wandered into the room looking for somewhere to settle.

Yasmin raised her eyes and, for the first time, looked straight at me. There was a slight trace of saliva at the corner of her mouth.

"Hell," she said. "I dream of hell."

The mother coughed. Yasmin returned her gaze to the floor.

On my way into town, I get a text from Jasper. He's been released and is heading for the coast. I send a text back thanking him for letting me know, confident that he will be able to read the sarcasm. He always does, even when there is no sarcasm to read. Text misinterpretation – it's one of the many issues Jasper and I grapple with since our relationship began to sour.

As I'm nearer the police station than home by this point, I decide to go and meet the Advocacy In Mind woman anyway. I've got some last minute shopping to do for tomorrow, my mother's 70th birthday.

Jasper and I first met in the street. He was busking near London Bridge. He reminded me of someone but I couldn't think of whom. I had to take a closer look. All kinds of feelings swept through me as I crouched down to put some money in his hat and pet his dog, including the sense that he recognised me too. He smiled – a raffish, vagabond kind of a smile – and asked me my name.

Two weeks later, we almost collided in another street. I was in my car and he wasn't looking where he was going. I beeped.

Shocked and strangely thrilled at seeing him again so clearly in my path, the wittiest opening gambit I could come up with was "Hi. How are you?"

He slumped sideways in a slow collapse onto the car bonnet. His coat was filthy and his eyes dull and yellow.

"My world has just been ripped apart," he said. "I have lost everything."

I bought him tea and cake in a little café. He wanted to smoke so we sat outside, among the hanging baskets and potted ferns, while the dog annoyed the people at the next table. Jasper apologised so charmingly to them that they ended up feeding it the remains of their club sandwiches.

The details of his story before I entered it are not mine to share. There had been high drama and terrible loss but not total devastation. He was sinking fast, he said; prey to various unscrupulous low-lifes and in a huge financial mess. A few days earlier, I had heard a similar tale from a young man who had been begging on the South Bank. I was prepared for a set-up.

We discovered we were neighbours, (he still had somewhere to live at least), and, even more bizarrely, had mutual friends in Spain. As the afternoon turned chilly, and with the needle on my bullshit-detector wavering, I decided that whatever was true or untrue he was undeniably fragile and in need of help. He once said that one of the many things we had in common was that we would go into the dark places where others wouldn't venture and my memories of that day are coated in a mixture of desire and revulsion, slaked with shadows. I drove him home and he waited in my kitchen, making uneasy conversation with a suspicious Tyrone, while I went upstairs to concoct a little package of remedies for him to take away. By the time I came back down, he and Tyrone were at the end of the garden playing football with Ricky. The dog was trying to make friends with the cats.

I leave the police station with some leaflets on advocacy volunteering, and a hazy picture of a fracas between Jasper and a Bermondsey wide boy with a pit bull. Jasper had tried to give him some unasked for dog training advice and got punched in the face. I have grown used to hearing about violence towards Jasper. He invites it because, being cleverer than the rest of us, he always knows best. He won't know for a while if he has to answer charges.

Riding that horrible, familiar feeling of knowing I can't keep him safe, I turn towards Covent Garden and the shops.

The meeting with my supervisor following Jasper's first visit to my house was stormy. Alexandra has been a wise counsellor to me all my professional life, but this time she just erupted. Where were my boundaries? Why did I take him into my home? What was I thinking?

I threatened to leave if she didn't stop ranting. I felt offended that she had so little trust in my judgement.

She reminded me of my first obligation – to my own safety and that of my children; and my second obligation – to create and preserve a distinct emotional boundary between my patient and myself.

"But he's not a patient. He's just someone I met."

She stared at me as if I was a stranger who had just revealed an awful truth.

"You're over-reacting," I continued. "He's down on his luck, and if I can help in some way..."

"No! He's too damaged. You have to pass on this one. Why are you telling me about him? Do you have any idea? Well, I'll tell you why. Because you want me to do exactly what I am doing. You want me to say No. Listen to yourself. You're terrified."

By this time Jasper was phoning me daily. He'd come by a couple of times a week and, while I cooked dinner, he'd help Tyrone with his maths or let Ricky climb all over him, the dog always at his feet, ready to step in if things got too rough. Then, when the kids had wandered off to do other things, he'd reveal more and more of his chaos.

He didn't seem to have any friends, though several ex-friends crept into our conversations. He spoke to his mother often on my kitchen phone, but usually ended up shouting at her because she refused to help him out. Then he would tell me what a wonderful mother I was, laugh and offer to do the washing-up.

Like an alchemist, he drew me into the crucible with him, dissolving what resistance I had left. As I watched myself fail to acknowledge the contaminants within the formula, a small voice whispered that all my preparations were for this moment. My leaden fear could be transmuted into a golden arc of selflessness. "You can do this," the voice said. "You can turn things around for him."

There is a message from Yasmin's mother on my answering machine. She thinks she left her Raybans behind. Would I mind taking a look? The symbolism makes me shiver slightly – shedding her blinkers. It's an opening.

No further news from Jasper. I hold the phone in my hand for the longest time, wanting to hear his voice yet, at the same time, not wanting to.

When he moved in, my close friends were horrified. Tina was on tour in the Far East and would be gone for months. Carlo had yet to appear on my horizon. The boys loved the dog and tolerated Jasper's more annoying habits as if he was one of the family already. He caught flu and needed nursing. It was more convenient to have him under my roof. I pretended it was purely pragmatic but I used to feel a terrible happiness when Jasper was lying quietly on the sofa in my living room, watching TV.

I'd stopped seeing Alexandra by this time because I refused to be deflected from my mission. Friends were another matter, not so easy to avoid. I claimed client confidentiality whenever the subject of my relationship with him came up, but it was obvious to everyone that he wasn't just passing through.

Sunday, and as the clan gathers for a birthday lunch at my mother's hilltop home, she greets me with a complaint. The deer have eaten all the dahlias and the terrace is not looking as it should. Murmuring conciliatory nothings, I am suddenly seized by a memory of Jasper being scolded by my mother for leaving the iron plugged in. This was in the days when I hauled him around with me anywhere and everywhere, anxious whenever he was out of my sight. We were going to a restaurant for dinner. He had brought a shirt for the occasion but it was creased. He had stopped dressing like a tramp. Trying his best to please her, he was bewildered when she got upset. His charm didn't work on everyone.

Watching Ricky shin up one of the pine trees which stand guard at the entrance to my mother's house, while his younger cousins look on in awe and the adults look apprehensive, I try to gauge how long I should give him before I intervene. Where is the line between over-protectiveness and neglect? I search for it in the branches and in Ricky's confident limbs. My mother's antipathy to Jasper, mirroring not only his troubled relationship with his own mother but the maternal role I had adopted in his life, was her attempt to nudge me away from the darkness before I fell in too deep. As Ricky clambers down of his own accord in time to join in the birthday toast, I raise my glass with the others and drink to her health.

Jasper, fortified by homeopathy and home cooking, began to shout. He could get hysterical about anything, from the thread count of the towels to the way I held my fork. His attacks came out of nowhere.

Homeopathically speaking, I understood that I was listening to the discharge of psychic pus. He wasn't shouting, he was howling. All the cleansing remedies I'd given seemed to be doing their work. However, due to my initial lack of regard for their power, the contaminants were erupting from the crucible in dangerous waves, blistering the surface of our fragile domestic arrangements and creating fissures in my heart as they fought dissolution. In homeopathy, the phenomenon of 'aggravation' or 'healing crisis' is considered by some to be an essential part of the process towards cure – the offending symptoms, in response to the well-chosen remedy, become temporarily more potent before subsiding. As the darkness wrestled itself to the ground in yet another ugly show of temper, I declined to agree. Like good intentions, the results of treatment can sometimes say more about the practitioner than the practice.

Months earlier, while Jasper was still enjoying being ferried around by me and I was enjoying a closer look at the British judicial system, making sure he kept his solicitor's appointments and turned up for his court appearances, he had thanked me for rescuing him. We were on our way back from his barrister's chambers. The meeting had gone well and for the first time a clear path could be glimpsed through the tangle of illness, debt and accusation.

"Oh no, I'm just a supporter," I had replied hurriedly, as the Blackwall tunnel loomed. "You know, one who travels alongside. I don't do rescuing."

"Hmm," he'd said, giving my arm a conspiratorial squeeze. "We'll have to see about that."

When I looked into his sullen, angry face, and as I tenderly tried to remove the dirt that clung to his clothing as if it was part of the weave, I felt as if I'd been looking at him for centuries, and was finally paying what I owed him, rewriting karma, absolving us both from any past or future misdeeds. In the underground river running beneath the tangled path, half-hidden by the rocks and bearded weeds, there dwelt a streak, a suspicion of something already completed. It was too late to demur. I had saved a man from drowning and was therefore responsible for his welfare.

As we leave my mother's house and I look back at the pines, the guardians of the gate, silhouetted in the grubby evening light, I imagine being able to quantify the steps I may have not taken, the thresholds I may have refused to cross, the dark places I may not have entered. Ricky and Tyrone start bickering over a piece of chewing gum and fill the car with noise. Tina tells them both to shut the fuck up. She's driving so I have nothing to do but be in a warm, slightly too small space with my children, possibly my favourite activity but so easily ruined by one false move. What if I were to hear Ricky disclose to a stranger that he dreams of hell? How does that point arrive in a child's short life with such eloquence? How can I get the mother to come for treatment? Ricky hits Tyrone in the eye with a full bottle of mineral water and Tina shouts, "That's it!", brings the car to a lurching halt on a dangerous bend, hands me the keys and says, "You drive."

I shift over to the driving seat, for a split second loathing them all but at the same time fishing in my bag for some Arnica for Tyrone, and some Rescue Remedy for the other two. As Alexandra once said, apropos a child-abuse case I brought to her, "You don't necessarily have to love your children, but you do have to give them love. You have to protect them until they're grown. Then you have to let them go."

When I told Jasper to go, I felt he had somehow won. Having weathered his many attempts to turn me from the Good Mother of his fantasies to the Bad Mother of his expectations, I suddenly lost the will to continue. A common scenario in the consulting-room, the transference of unresolved parental issues onto the therapist, had followed me into my kitchen. Having always prided myself on skilful handling of this particular challenge to my integrity as a homeopath, refusing to take the bait and join the drama triangle dance, I had moved from being his Rescuer to the Victim of his anger and then, by rejecting him, to the Bad Mother, the Persecutor, at last.

When he refused to leave, challenging me to phone the police, I felt such a profound sense of being met by all my own demons that we spent the night drawing out of each other's mouths the most venomous insults we could think of until it became so absurd we ended up laughing hysterically in a heap, the dog barking at us with a puzzled ferocity.

"You bring out the worst in me," I said.

"I know," he replied, stroking the dog's soft brow. "That's why I'm here."

On Monday, Yasmin's mother calls again. I had found the sunglasses down the side of the sofa. She is very grateful, and I can hear the embarrassment in her voice as we talk. She sounds softer. It's like we know each other now. I have been a witness to her daughter's existential pain. I'm almost family.

The doorbell rings, and through the frosted glass I see a familiar outline.

"Ta da!" he says, when I open the door, "Bad penny."

"Hay fever tablets?" I step aside as the dog bounds in, making straight for the kitchen and the cat food.

"Well, you know, easier than actually trying to EXPLAIN!" He looks awful. His left cheek is swollen. He can't quite make eye contact. "For a bunch of bastard police they were actually very nice."

"I thought we agreed, no more court cases?"

"Frosty? Shall I go? Come on, dog." He looks beyond me towards the kitchen. "Oh, but I'll be wanting my suit. I'm due back at the station on the 19th."

"I'll put the kettle on," I say, because the last thing I want is for him to go.

"Oh, okay then. And can I have a bath?"

Jasper once accused me of collecting his hair from the plughole in the bath in order to do some kind of voodoo on him behind his back. I explained the concept of cleaning up after oneself in such a patronising tone that he didn't speak to me for the rest of the day.

After his bath, we walk to the park, like old times. I'm so pissed off that he is in trouble again. No longer sick or crippled by circumstances, he's plunging backwards into the river and I think that this time I just might let him drown.

We sit under a favourite tree while the dog ingratiates itself with a group of picnickers who throw it some chicken bones.

Jasper tells me that he's not here to ask for my help. I wait, hoping he'll tell me why he is here. The dog bounds across the grass, a terrier on its tail.

His mobile rings. It's his mother. I wander over to the picnickers to thank them for being kind to the dog and, when I return, he says his mother doesn't understand why I still put up with him.

Some weeks after our night of venomous fury, as we negotiated a more peaceful co-existence which involved not talking very much, I was in my cellar hunting for a pair of pliers when I glanced down and saw the postcard that had been in my possession since I was a teenager and which, for some reason that I never stopped to think about, was always on display wherever I lived, usually gracing a mantle-piece or pinned to a wall.

A year or so before, I had relegated it to the cellar, propping it up against an old paint tin on one of the dusty shelves where I rarely looked. I had no idea why I should have demoted it and didn't stop to think about that either. Its continued existence was miraculous, given the number of times I'd moved house. The image, a reproduction of an old painting, was so familiar – a part of my life, a part of myself. Nevertheless, I had sent it down the back stairs to the underworld.

The man in the painting looked out at me from beneath a veneer of grime. Jasper's face – that's where I'd seen him before. Even the eyebrows were the same. I could almost hear the cascade of cosmic tumblers falling around me like a collection of empty paint cans dropping randomly onto a hard cellar floor, yet landing in a mysteriously precise formation. Until that moment I hadn't recognised Jasper as the man in the painting. To what extent had I recognised the man in the painting, all those years ago, as the foreshadow of someone yet to come? Was all this nurturing of mine dependent on an image from the 16th century, a teenage crush which had endured down the years until it found me skating on very thin ice in a street quite close to London Bridge? Did I really only ever care about him because of his looks?

I showed the postcard to him and he flinched. Our non-verbal communication had become so refined by this point, we were like swimmers weaving patterns in the water, which rippled – sometimes together, but mostly apart. The roles of Victim, Rescuer and Persecutor writhed in a complicated heap at the bottom of the river, like eels bred from electrical disturbances and mud.

To celebrate my shallowness we took Tyrone and Ricky to the circus.

I had been growing increasingly concerned about the effect Jasper's moods were having on the boys, who had both witnessed several arguments between us. Tyrone tended to stick up for whomever his devastatingly logical mind perceived as being in the right. The often confused beginnings of the latest altercation became delineated by his sense of fairness. Usually he decided we were both just stupid. My rationale for allowing him to become involved was a hope that he would continue to feel comfortable in airing all his own unresolved parental issues while he was still living with me – his tender, teenage manliness flip-flopping with his childlike insistence on being, alongside Tina and Ricky, the centre of his mother's world.

For Ricky, who was prone to tantrums of his own, the verbal aggression Jasper displayed was all part of some Boys Own adventure or tribal holler in the jungle. He might as well have been swinging on vines.

I found it troubling that Ricky was so little troubled and as we sat together in the Big Top, while a third rate troupe of acrobats attempted a wobbly pyramid, I reached for his hand. Engrossed in trying to stick popcorn up his nostrils and blow it out again, he turned away from me and moved a little closer to Jasper. What should a good mother do?

Jasper once told me that if you want to make a man happy, ask him to fix something and then tell him how clever he is when he's done it. My mother once told me that if you want a man to do anything, get him to think it's his idea.

Amalgamating these strategies, I made a list of DIY chores and handed it to him. As he worked through the items I praised his carpentry skills, his plumbing acumen and his prowess with electrics and kept adding more to the list. In a house like ours, this was not difficult.

Jasper started to leave the house quite early in the morning and stay out all day, sometimes all night. Having rediscovered his considerable cleverness with the inanimate, he had gone home and begun to tackle the mess. If he was going to spend all his time mending things, he told me, he might as well start with his own.

His mother, impressed by his sudden transformation into Mr Fixit, invited him to her house on the coast. He took his bag of tools with him.

Before he left, we wept together for all the craziness and congratulated each other on our achievements.

As I waved goodbye at the station I felt, for a short while at least, that I would be happy to never see him again.

On Wednesday, Yasmin's mother leaves me another message. She has decided to cancel Yasmin's next appointment with me because it's too far to travel. As these are her very words, I cannot help but catch their metaphorical significance.

Jasper, who, after our walk in the park had gone back to his own house to check the mail and stayed there, texts me a link to a holiday website. He thinks we should go on a trip.

I weigh these two telephonic events, trying to decide what level of action and non-action is required by each.

Yasmin's mother also says that Yasmin has been crying a lot since last week. I get the feeling she thinks this is a bad thing. My conviction that Yasmin needs rescuing from a childhood spent being unable to communicate with those whom she depends on for her welfare spins in the space now vacant again in my appointments book. The most I can do here may already have been done. I reach for my directory of London homeopaths and look up a number of someone I can recommend nearer home. I put the Raybans in an envelope.

The thought of travelling further with Jasper is put on hold during all this while my internal switchboard constructs a busy signal from the acreage of my reclaimed boundary. Alone in the silence, the possibilities contained in my next move reverberate under my feet as if detecting the pulsing of an echo – like standing on a river bank, which holds the promise of something waiting on the other side, some future reflection of what is already there, beyond the mystery of deep water.

Reunion

> *'I never even thought about whether or not they understand what I'm doing... the emotional reaction is all that matters. As long as there's some feeling of communication, it isn't necessary that it be understood.'*
>
> *John Coltrane*

One of the virtues of a long weekend with my old friends from art school is their lack of interest in homeopathy. Nobody wants me to heal them. It's a miracle. Other praiseworthy features include their generosity of spirit, their cooking skills and their continual pursuit of the creative life.

We walk across the marshes in the pouring rain just so we can catch the ferry back; and run around the beach photographing each other photographing every thing else.

"It's a college project," Hayden remarks, posing winsomely against the skyline.

"I'm going to call this one, 'Hayden – winsome pose,' Gerry says, as I fall over him and we roll together down the dune.

"You read my mind," I say, as we lie locked in a gritty hug at the bottom.

"I always could," he replies. "You know that."

Hayden and Gerry have been married for years. Before they got together, Gerry and I shared a basement flat with Bill and Lenny, who are also here. We've known each other so long, we just pick up mid-sentence.

The out-of-season mansion on the edge of the sands, buffeted by gales from the North Sea; the damply genteel town where dowagers race their electric scooters down the promenade and teenagers loll politely outside the chip-shop, where the marshes lie about on all sides and brackish lagoons lurk behind the shingle ridge; the long walks and the early evening sessions in the pub; the gourmet cooking in the cavernous kitchen; dinner and more talk, more laughter. It's perfect.

Except it's not. Camille is expected too, but hasn't turned up, and Hayden is beginning to fret.

"She's still not answering."

"Probably forgot to shave her legs and had to turn back," Lenny says.

Bill looks up to the ceiling. "Do you remember that bloke you hit, Len, when Camille was working on the Gillette account?"

Hayden starts to collect plates with a frisson of irritation. "She's a day late, you morons. Why hasn't she rung, texted? Anybody?"

I make a bad joke about Camille not being razor-sharp and Gerry mimes for me to sshh behind Hayden's retreating back. I suddenly feel sick. You mean, that wasn't funny? Oh, I'm sorry. Don't withdraw, Hayden... but she's gone. Into the kitchen to cause a clatter.

If you always have to take yourself with you, I think, you might as well stay at home.

Camille arrives while we are finishing off the cheese, her fine cheekbones streaked with mascara and her long blonde hair in disarray. Milo has walked out on her, she says. It happened just yesterday morning.

"Where are the children?" Lenny wants to know. We all, of course, want to know everything and crowd round her, but Camille is now sobbing hysterically in Hayden's arms and can no longer speak. Bill and Lenny continue to fire who, why, where, what, when questions, while Hayden rocks Camille like a baby. I put the kettle on. Gerry reaches for the scotch.

Milo is Camille's third husband and consequently 'not one of us.' I'm not sure anybody ever liked him very much but, as with all our chosen partners, we have tried to include him – a bit. He wasn't invited this weekend, which apparently has nothing to do with his sudden decision to leave. Camille manages to describe driving here, alone, in the dark – a feat of which she is proud.

"I just had to get to you guys," she blubbers.

Hayden and I exchange looks. I know she's not thinking what I'm thinking because I'm thinking that what Camille needs right now is a strong dose of Pulsatilla and I have some upstairs. But I wait. It's almost unbearable watching my dear friend in such pain. I would do anything to comfort her. As Bill blinks rapidly into the middle distance and Lenny marches into the garden as if looking for someone to kill, Hayden straightens up and says,

"Right, we're all going to go to bed now, and everything will seem much better in the morning after a good night's sleep."

"Noooo," Camille howls, "it will not. He's left me. I want to die."

Gerry finds me on the landing.

"What?" he says.

"I'm thinking," I reply. "Can't you tell what?"

"Ha ha, very funny."

I look at the young man I used to know inside the paunchy, middle-aged figure in front of me. We were having such a nice time.

"I want to give Camille a remedy but I don't know if she'll take it and, maybe, crying is what she needs to do – exhausting yet cleansing."

"It's bloody awful. Like listening to a..." He stops as if he realises he's about to sound boorish. "Well, you're the expert. Do whatever. She may knock it out of your hand but..."

"Hayden's more for the Valium approach, I feel."

"Tried and tested."

There is a pause, neither of us in the mood for an argument. In the silence, I detect a similar lack of noise from below.

"She's stopped," Gerry realises at the same time as I do. "Thank fucking Christ."

Camille staggers up the stairs towards us.

"Hey, guys, where's the bathroom?" Her face is a mask of miserable blotchy swellings, her panda eyes still brimming.

"Let me show you." Gerry holds out his hand. "We have three."

She wraps her arms around me and hugs me to her. I wrap my arms around her. "Can I sleep in your room tonight?" she asks. "I really don't want to be alone."

Lying in the dark, listening to Camille's breathing, now calm and deeply, alluringly asleep, I reflect on the roles we have so readily adopted in the house. Hayden and Gerry, the parents; Camille, the baby; me, the big sister; Bill and Lenny, the older brothers, possibly bent on revenge. I try to remember if it was always like this.

What I do remember, with a nasty little stab of pain, is feeling very hurt when Camille didn't make it to my homeopathic college graduation. She begged off with some lame excuse but I knew it was because she thought I was making a terrible mistake. A successful art director herself, she couldn't understand why I should give up my career as a photographer, a life spent dealing with the superficial, to train in some ridiculous medical system that required years of study and held little prospect of big bucks. I'm surprised that it still rankles all these years later, and reach into my lexicon of emotions for the name of the feeling.

Hostility? No. Jealousy? No. Outrage? Certainly not. Rejection? Close. Abandonment? Yes.

Come to think of it, although the others came it was as if unwillingly. They all believe it's nothing to do with them, I know – another unmentionable like Gerry's paunch, or Bill's twitch or Hayden's varicose veins. As if I've grown a homeopathy wart on my chin.

Once in bed, Camille had taken the Pulsatilla I offered her with a kind of meek aplomb and, within minutes, was smiling. Her last words before going to sleep were, "All men are bastards. I feel lovely and warm inside."

I was surprised at how easy it was. I guess she didn't have the energy to protest. Slip it in while they're defenceless has never been my favourite strategy, but sometimes it's the only way. And now she's peacefully sleeping, and I'm restlessly poking at a past hurt.

Camille wakes around three and starts snivelling. I pop another Pulsatilla in her mouth and within seconds she is out again. The waves crash on the rocks below as I drift. I yearn to be outside.

Breakfast next morning is long, drawn-out and loaded. Camille is curled up next to Lenny on the sofa, like the young lovers they were thirty years before. Gerry, Bill and I are sprawled in large, design-led armchairs. Hayden's having a shower.

Some highlights:

Lenny: "What's a husband or three when you got me?"

Gerry: "You're no longer fit for purpose, mate."

To Bill: "Sorry I woke you up this morning, Billy Boy. I thought you were..."

Bill: "It's fine, I was awake already. Just listening to my thoughts."

Gerry: "What, like 'Kill ALL of them?'"

Camille, snuggling even closer: "Come with me to the phone shop, Len?"

Bill: "Where do you think you are? They've barely heard of the crystal detector receiver here."

Gerry: "Have one of mine. I've got three."

Camille: "He said that I oppressed him. 'I feel oppressed by you' were his very words."

Lenny: "Bastard."

Gerry: "And was that in a dialectical sense?"

Camille: "Excuse me?"

Gerry: "Has Milo even read Hegel?"

Bill: "Gerry, you're not helping."

Gerry: "It's all the threes, they're messing with my head. Hasn't anyone got any pot?"

Camille: "Hey, guess what. I had a homeopathy sleeping-pill last night, and it worked."

No one says anything.

I haven't said anything for ages, too busy sifting the details of Camille's story. Milo's gone AWOL. Last week the live-in nanny suddenly resigned. Camille's mother has the children, one from each husband, the youngest barely out of nappies. The phone's lost or broken, but it doesn't matter because Camille's mother has all our numbers now and we all have hers and somebody already rang her last night to say Camille had arrived safely. Camille is still looking pale and puffy-eyed but otherwise better.

Everyone looks at me.

Me: "It was nothing." I force a smile.

Gerry: "Wretched placebo."

Lenny: "What did you give her?"

Me: "It's called Pulsatilla. It's a..."

Bill: "Tears of Venus."

Me: "What?"

Bill: "Tears of Venus. Pulsatilla. It's a kind of anemone.

Me: "Oh, yes..."

Lenny: "And?"

Bill: "Well, Adonis, ha ha, was murdered by Ares who was jealous of his affair with Aphrodite."

Gerry: "Triple A."

Bill: "Oh yeah, never noticed. To continue... Ares got him right in the guts during a hunting expedition. He'd disguised himself as a wild boar, like you do. Adonis's spilled blood mingled with Aphrodite's tears and produced the anemone, from the Greek, anemos, meaning wind. Pulsatilla. Anemone. Windflower. Tears of Venus."

We all stare at Bill now.

Bill: "My Open University degree. Classics, remember?"

Hayden appears fully dressed and suggests we walk across the dunes before it rains and then go to the pub for lunch.

Gerry: "Sorry, shouldn't that be tears of Aphrodite?"

Lenny: "Nit-picker. Look at her, she is Venus."

Camille, lip trembling slightly: "Venus does sound nicer, doesn't it."

Me: "That's brilliant, Bill. I never knew that. Thanks."

Bill: "Well, it was the tears, wasn't it, made me remember."

Gerry: "Someone should have told Adonis, three's a crowd."

Camille: starting to cry: "Oh, do you mean... do you think he's met someone else?"

Gerry had learnt to read my mind while teaching me chess during our first summer at art school. However, what has always rankled with him slightly is that I learnt to read his first.

He had been taught the game during an acid trip some years before and, consequently, had an idiosyncratic vision of shape, rhythm and design that I followed blindly for a while, as if learning Braille – the method was clear from the beginning but the meaning remained mysteriously opaque, hidden by the cataract of my linear thinking.

On slow afternoons we would go home early, sit in the shade on the sunken terrace behind our flat, drink tea and play until the midges drove us inside. He kept up an incessant commentary, a kind of lucid drivel which encompassed history, art, music, maths, psychoanalysis, politics and military strategy, designed to strengthen my resistance to distraction and my ability to focus. He introduced me to jazz and cubism at the same time, triangulating them with the chess, daring me to decode a world made up of geometry, syncopation and bluff. Gradually, I learnt to look beyond his folded diagrams until one day I suddenly saw it too. The whole thing. And equally, the whole Gerry.

When I started being able to win an occasional game from him, the commentary thankfully stopped as he found himself shifting to a less advantageous position, but one that he had helped to create. He went very quiet and stalked my thoughts until he could undermine any trajectory I had planned by just letting me know he was on to me. It was symbiosis of a kind. Less a psychic connection, more a cerebral twinning.

This was made easier by a common backdrop to our early lives – we had both been brought up as Catholics. Abandoning the Holy Trinity was a sin we shared, and was not to be spoken of to anyone else. His working-class, Northern Irish family and my middle-class, Mediterranean clan, though different in so many ways, had similarly handed us and our education over to the care of monks and nuns at a very early age. We were only just beginning to assess the damage.

Sometimes we'd play Vatican chess – the Queen was the Pope and the King, God. The pawns were choirboys, under particular threat from the bishops. The knights were unicorns, the remnants of pre-Christian paganism, and the rooks were the Swiss guards. The board was the banks of the Tiber. Given that, whoever won, checkmate symbolised the death of Catholicism, of which we were both heartily in favour, we needed a little competitive edge. So we settled on a bit of historical in-fighting. White was the Holy See and black, the Jesuits, whose founder, St Ignatius of Loyola, the original black pope, was another potent hate figure in our lives. Gerry would intone Ignatius's most famous line: 'I will believe that the white that I see is black if the hierarchical Church so defines it' over every checkmated God and then put on some Miles Davies and make another pot of tea. It was pretty intense and verged on disturbing. When Hayden appeared at the start of the autumn term, fresh from the Home Counties, I was more than happy to step back and let her woo him away. Camille had jostled for position a bit, while fending off a love-sick Lenny, but it had all turned out for the best, although Camille has been left three times now, holding three different babies by three different men, so not the best for her.

Gerry taught me that that one's opponent is always one's greatest teacher and that the game is often over before it has begun. Even now he wears his twelve-roomed mansion by the sea and his gold American Express card with a halo of guilt and a sprinkling of shame.

Walking back from the pub, Hayden, Camille and I linger behind the others and find a bench to sit on. The sun has appeared from under the drizzle and the seafront sparkles with a new light. Like our summit meetings of old, when we convened to discuss the trouble with men, we melt into a conversation that seems, in the interim, to have been running along all on its own.

Hayden had got annoyed with Gerry in the pub for nothing really, and is grumbling about him generally. Camille is reliving Milo's exit for the millionth time and Hayden gets a bit snappy with her too, suggesting that she'd better get over that bit, horrible though it was, and formulate a plan. I query whether a plan is what is actually needed and suggest that Camille just sits still, so to speak, and waits.

Hayden, who had gone on to mention lawyers and settlements, frowns at me.

"I'm sure that's very Zen but not really practical, is it?"

I shrug with what I hope looks like Zen-like calm. I can't help but silently wonder if her hormones need tweaking.

Camille starts to talk about her father's suicide. He left for the beach one day and never returned. The official verdict was accidental death, as he hadn't left a note. Camille was fourteen and she struggled through half a decade of ineffectual misery until art school opened a door to her creativity, and her drive to succeed was unleashed. Though Hayden and I have heard this story often of course, it moves us every time. We sit beside her, holding a hand each while she weeps, until Lenny appears from behind a lamppost and takes a photo of us.

"Ah, look, you see – I got you. The three witches."

He remains standing where he is, as if not daring to cross an invisible line.

Camille removes her hand from mine and holds it out to him.

"I should have married you, shouldn't I, after all? I'm an idiot."

"Oh, pur-lease," Hayden says out of the corner of her mouth, so that Lenny can't hear, then slowly rises in a creaky sort of way and crosses the short distance between us and him to look at the picture on his digital screen.

"I'm going to take one of you lot later as the three wise monkeys," she says to Lenny, "or should that be the three foolish old men?"

"That'll be it," Lenny says. "Worth-Nothing, Know-Nothing and Good-For-Nothing. Anyway, I've come to find you because Bill's asleep and Gerry's disappeared into his office. I got bored."

He grins at us and it seems to me that for Lenny, as for Camille, time has stood still in some unmagical way and age is hardly even a veneer. A light patina perhaps, but one that doesn't seem to have much to do with maturity or experience.

"Arrested development," I say out loud, though not meaning to.

"Indubitably," Lenny nods.

"I think I need another one of your pills," Camille says. "Like right now."

We walk back to the house.

Gerry, in his razor-sharp way, has been watching the threes mount up. Like me, he's calculating opposites, dialectic duos – past and present, cause and effect, self and other, leave-taking and reunion – and they keep adding up to three. His remark in the pub that had so annoyed Hayden had been that there were three of us in the group whose name contains a 'y'.

"Why?" he pleaded. "Oh, why now did I notice the three 'y's?"

This had made Bill laugh, and then it was Bill's turn to be silly but he couldn't think of anything. Hayden said she felt embarrassed for them both. In fact, Bill, while innocently showing off his knowledge of Greek mythology, has added to the equation but I think he's oblivious to the wider meaning of his words. If Milo's disappearance is to do with another woman, the nanny perhaps, it would again add up to three.

Lenny is now showing Bill and Gerry the three witches photo on his iPad.

"What a coven of posers," Gerry scoffs.

I'm about to tell him that we had been discussing Camille's drowned dad at the time and that, given our location and the circumstances, it had been a particularly poignant moment when Hayden lurches forward and hits him on the side of his head.

"Ow!" he cries.

"That's for being stupid," she says. "And this..." She hits him again.

"Hayden! Ow! Fuck off!"

"... is for being a man."

She storms upstairs.

A shy, pretty flower whose leaves produce a corrosive juice, Pulsatilla grows in clusters. There is an enormous variety of subspecies, ranging through all the hues from near white to near black. It thrives on dry sandy soil with little need for water, and flowers in the early spring, when the air is still cool. Known as the windflower, it moves with the slightest breeze, pliable and easily influenced.

The poisonous properties of Pulsatilla, and therefore its healing potential, have been known for centuries and were described by Pliny, Galen and Dioscorides. However, in homeopathy, knowing the toxicology of a substance is not enough. To understand the classic image of the Pulsatilla state, firstly the behavioural characteristics of shyness, a mild, yielding disposition and a need for company are added to the variability of physical symptoms, lack of thirst and desire for cool air, all mirrored aspects of the plant. The fluid imbalance indicated by the lack of thirst is confirmed by an easy tearfulness.

Focusing in on the need for company, what distinguishes Pulsatilla from other gregarious types is that being alone feels like having been abandoned, and abandonment is Pulsatilla's greatest fear.

Those who have difficulty passing the major milestones of separation and growing up, which require abandoning the safety of the infantile, the shelter of the known, the protection of the parents, and who respond with a clingy weepiness or a reluctance to let go will benefit from a few judicious doses of Pulsatilla. Mothers of shy, clingy small children will at this point understand the remedy perfectly, and there is usually something child-like in the adult Pulsatilla patient's behaviour which draws forth feelings of affectionate concern from the homeopath. Whenever I find myself resisting the urge to give a patient a cuddle, I write 'Pulsatilla?' in the margin of my notes.

However, beyond the everyday struggles of the developing human, there is another class of patients – those who have in reality been abandoned. Knowing the causation, the aetiology, of a state is often a shortcut to knowing the right remedy – understanding the patient's response to the trauma is how we join the dots.

First year homeopathy students and keen home-prescribers would probably all have given Camille some Ignatia when she first arrived. I probably would too, if it wasn't Camille, and if it wasn't for her dad. Ignatia is the first remedy one learns to use for acute grief and is particularly indicated when grief turns into hysteria.

St Ignatius's bean, named in honour of the black pope himself, was brought to Europe from the Philippines by the Jesuits in the 17th century, making it, when compared to Pulsatilla, a relative newcomer in the pharmacopeia. Containing a large amount of Strychnine, it produces among other things, tetanic spasms, twitches, the risus sardonicus, (or sardonic smile – a grimace caused by paralysis of the facial muscles), uncontrollable weeping, nausea, insomnia, a sensation of emptiness in the stomach and a lump in the throat. The rollercoaster of emotions brought on by the loss of a loved one mimics these symptoms of instability and Ignatia, used homeopathically, can act as a handrail through difficult times of bereavement, enabling the grief to be assimilated so that it doesn't overwhelm.
In contrast to Pulsatilla's sense of abandonment, Ignatia's grief concerns the loss of an ideal and it is the shattered dream that is mourned rather than the empty, lonely space. Collapsing illusions, crumbling castles in the air, such as loss of faith in religion, or in a relationship that has failed to meet expectations, require the construction of a new set of moves on a destabilised board. The remedy made from Ignatia will help this process as effectively as it will assist after an actual death, so that the meaning of the loss can be explored.

Both Pulsatilla and Ignatia yearn in different ways for reunion with the primal forces of our innocent beginnings, to furnish the emptiness that accompanies the disillusionment of growing-up. Who among us, I wonder, doesn't at some time need either of these remedies, or both?

Tonight, our last, Hayden has booked a table at the most expensive restaurant in town. Its courtyard is home to an oak that is reputed to be 400 years old. Bill and I, the only arboreally inquisitive members of the group, stand beneath it during a break between courses and discuss history. He observes that ours is like the tree, scarred yet solid.

"You can hug it if you like," I say, "I won't tell."

"Nah, you've probably got a secret camera in your earring or something. It'll be all over Facebook by tomorrow."

He leans against the trunk and, with a sigh, tells me he thinks he's become neurotic about all sorts of things. He starts to list them so I interrupt by telling him he's not neurotic but possibly spends too much time thinking.

"Like you, you mean? You and Gerry were always the thinkers, always with your nose in a bloody book. God, I love that man."

"Me too. I love you all, actually."

"Do you?" He sighs again. "Sometimes I get the feeling, especially when you go quiet, that you think you're better than us because you've got your voodoo thing and we don't..."

"Well, I..."

"What about Camille though? It's not looking good, is it? Though she's definitely better than she would be. Should I try and get hold of Milo? Duff him up a bit psychologically? Maybe I should invite him to my men's group."

"Um..."

"Pulsatilla. Who'd have thought it?"

Gerry texts me from the dining room to say the desserts have arrived. As we go back inside, I make a detour to the loo. It is upholstered in blood red – walls, carpet, ceiling, like a womb, I think. On a shelf above the washbasin is a row of old paperbacks. I spy 'The End Of The Affair' by

Graham Greene, pluck it from its resting place, open it and read the first lines.

'A story has no beginning or end: arbitrarily one chooses that moment of experience from which to look back or from which to look ahead.'

I suppose that in a history of Catholicism, Greene, Hegel and Ignatius would lie in a pleasingly alphabetical stream quite close together in the index. How I'd love to hear them slug it out over the port.

In bed that night I get another text from Gerry. He's still up and has been Googling. According to an article in the Journal of the American Statistical Association, Jesuits tend to die in threes. If I don't believe him, I can get up and read it for myself.

I pad quietly to his office. His shaved head, like a helmet, gleams in the light from an anglepoise on his desk. He swivels round with a sardonic smile.

"You are mad," I say.

"Yes, but I'm having so much fun. Look." He pats the chair next to him.

It is true. Jesuits tend to die in threes. I'm thrilled.

We scroll through pages and pages of conspiracy theories and sex abuse scandals until the gothic abomination of it all starts to sound like the garbled pitch for a particularly bad horror movie.

"We didn't have the internet, did we?" he mutters. "We had to play fucking chess."

"Well, we weren't sexually abused either. Just indoctrinated."

"A more ordinary madness, you mean?"

To antidote the rising tide of nausea, we decide to hunt for unicorns and trawl through dozens of images, mostly ghastly kitsch stuff, until we find a lovely drawing by Leonardo Da Vinci.

"Oh look, 'Maiden with Unicorn' – it's Camille," I say, excitedly.

"Like a virgin," Gerry replies as he clicks on YouTube and searches for Madonna videos. "Wanna dance?"

When I return to my room, Camille is snoring in perfect time to the sound of the waves, which have lost their urgency and calmly swish and whoosh under the window. I pull back the curtain and peer out. Gerry is standing on the lawn, looking up at the sky, which is littered with stars. I bet he's trying to find Venus.

I open the window.

"Hey, your eminence," I whisper. "It's over there."

As he turns towards me, I point randomly upwards.

"Slightly to the left of… thingy."

"Wrong," he hisses back. "I just looked it up. It's currently retrograde which means it's over there."

He wobbles towards the edge of the garden and points to the jetty below, smothered now at high tide. The sea looks almost gelatinous.

"I caught a unicorn once," he shouts against the sound of the waves, "or was it a sea horse? Anyway, it was this big."

He stretches his arms wide and falls over backwards. One Courvoisier too many.

I close the window and hurry downstairs.

We sit on a flat piece of rock, while I hold a bag of frozen peas to the back of Gerry's head.

"Have you ever heard of Arnica?" I enquire.

"Yeah, heavy metal band aren't they. Quite well-known in the '80s, but since then their star has waned though they're all fabulously rich due to some astute investing by their manager, Garfield Crouch the third, scion of the House of Crouch, old money you know, and Masonic Grand Wizard. Their last hit, 'Satan on Drugs,' won the award for best use of the glottal stop in a musical category. Broadway beckoned but they all retired to Miami instead. Look at that wave, there for the taking. Do you surf?"

"It's a homeopathic remedy," I reply. "Good for bangs on the head and subsequent lunatic ravings."

"I don't need Pulsatilla then?"

"No, but I think Hayden needs... something."

"From you? Verily, my queen is grumpy. It cannot be ignored."

"Possibly, but I was thinking more from you."

"Right. I'll have my people get in touch with my other people straight after breakfast."

He tries to get up and groans.

"Or lunch. By the way, Bill got it slightly wrong about the anemone. The Greco-Roman thing. I looked that up too. It was a different flower."

"Will you tell him?"

"I doubt it. With friends like these... who needs anemones?"

I rise and help him to his feet. God, he's heavy.

He takes my arm and we climb the few steps back to the garden.

"'Who is the third who walks always beside you?' – always been one of my favourite lines," he says, squeezing my elbow.

"I know," I reply. "I was there, remember?"

Saying goodbye next morning is difficult for everyone. However, Hayden's going back to London with Camille until the nanny agency finds a replacement and is talking excitedly about all the exhibitions she's going to see. Lenny and I are already booked for Sunday lunch at Camille's the following weekend, and Bill's staying on a few extra days with Gerry so that they can watch horror movies in the dark and eat popcorn without anyone complaining about their diets.

We all hug and re-hug till we're breathless and, though Camille is remarkably dry-eyed, I feel I could cry at any moment. Gerry takes a photo of me and offers it around.

"I'm going to call this one, 'Last night a pea-bag saved my life'," he says.

"Oh, gross," says Lenny. "Got your old trouble back have you, Ger?"

"No, you idiot, not piss-bag, pea-bag. P-e-a."

Hayden grabs me again and whispers in my ear, "Sometimes, I just want to kill him."

"You're heroic," I whisper back.

Camille joins us.

"Are you talking about me?" she asks.

"No, get in the car, I'm coming," Hayden snaps, as she fishes a scarf and sunglasses from her handbag and puts them on.

"Heraldry for a new era," she says, looking over her glasses at me. "Primark, 50p."

We drive off in convoy, Camille and Hayden leading the way, me in the middle and, at the rear, Lenny, who toots loudly and nearly unseats a passing dowager.

"Be seeing you," Gerry yells, as Bill's whole body moves in a spasmodic wave.

By the time I reach the motorway, I'm in need of a break. I stop at the first service station I come to and, over a cup of watery tea, look through all the photos I've taken in the last few days. In the album of our shared history they are just fleeting blurs of light and I realise that, in the hundreds of images we've produced this weekend, there will not be one among them of us all together. Somebody was always behind the lens, looking on.

The metaphors we live by may have changed in the intervening years, and our banter may at times contain barbs designed to wound, but, like the spiral horn of the unicorn which could neutralise poison and purify water, their apparent sharpness and the blood they spill have more in common with mythology than truth. Small abandonments of feeling that never seriously threaten the tenacity of our bond.

Reaching further into my bag for a tissue, I find a CD I've never seen before. On the case is a scrawled message.

"For the ride home. G."

Back in the car, I slot it into the CD player. It's Miles Davis playing 'Some Day My Prince Will Come', the title track from an album I know well. As Gerry has told me a thousand times, it was the last recording Miles made with John Coltrane in the band before the young pretender struck out on his own.

I imagine the delight Gerry took in planting it when I wasn't looking, a sardonic smile flickering at the corners of his mind as he pictured me, young, eager and confused all those years ago, gamely plotting my next move.

Faking It

> *'Darwinian theory tells us that an interest in truth is not needed for survival or reproduction. More often it is a disadvantage. Deception is common among primates and birds.'*
>
> *John Gray – Straw Dogs*

Remi and I are trudging against a biting November wind along a desolate piece of dockland.

"It's here somewhere," he mutters, feeling his pockets. "Shit, I can't find the code."

"Remi, we haven't found the building yet, let alone a door or anything. Maybe it's back that way."

I look behind me at the swathe of nothingness we have already negotiated. There's not even any traffic. As London dual carriageways go, this one's eerily empty and, despite being slightly lost, I feel strangely at peace. It's just us and the landscape.

"I'll phone," Remi decides, gingerly pressing numbers as if picking out a tune on an old and unreliable instrument. Head down, he wanders round in circles, leaning in and out of the wind as he tries to get a signal even though we are somewhere very flat and devoid of tall buildings. For a scientist he's impressively low-tech. Maybe that's why we get along.

He gives me the thumbs up and puts the phone back in his pocket.

"They're waiting for us," he says, breathlessly. "Well, come on!"

At the entrance to the warehouse we are greeted by two young men. They introduce themselves as Corin and Dave and one of them signs us in on a piece of chipped white-board dangling on a hook.

"Urgent need for door code?" I whisper to Remi, who pretends not to hear.

Corin and Dave usher us speedily down to the basement, where we find several elderly patrons of the museum and other assorted suits quaffing milky tea in a dilapidated office. The light is dim and has a greenish tinge, making everyone look a bit dead.

Lord Somebody or Other introduces Remi, recipient of the museum's latest bursary, to polite applause. I am ignored, though Remi tries to include me then gives up as he is offered to the throng who quickly crowd round him, pecking at his aura like hungry birds.

As Remi has decided he's not ready to let his new benefactors know he's gay, I've come along as his pretend girlfriend. Not so much because being gay is a handicap in the museum world, far from it, but because his Pakistani parents are still unaware of their youngest son's half-in half-out closet routine. I have no opinion worth mentioning on this other than their loss is my gain and, hoping to catch sight of some hidden artefacts in this secret underground storehouse, I have armed myself with camera and notebook. I don't mind being ignored in the least. I want to snoop.

However, it soon becomes apparent that this will not be possible as we are all going to be kept on a very tight rein throughout the tour. No deviation from the path will be permitted as we may get lost, which I interpret as not to be trusted. We get given the fire drill and other health and safety procedures, and are ordered to leave our handbags behind.

I take the camera and notebook out of my bag and stuff them in my pockets, catching Corin's, or is it Dave's, eye as I do. Curators are probably all good at spotting detail. Then again, maybe I just look shifty. Remi gives me a slight shove as we proceed.

After a long sojourn in the paleontology room, during which Remi is called upon to justify the museum's largesse towards him by outlining his impending project (something to do with DNA and rat skeletons), and Corin/Dave proudly unveils his new acquisition (a chest of drawers full of rat skeletons and other bits of dead rodent awaiting classification), we move on to the centre of the hoard. Trailing daringly behind the others, I take a few photos of antlers and dogs' teeth but I'm yet to get excited. Dave/Corin waits for me at the door.

As I enter the great hall of wonders, anticipating untold treasures, I hear somebody, possibly that geeky looking man who I think is Corin and Dave's boss, announce proudly that "Ninety five per cent of the museum's stock is right here."

I confront a series of massive shapes shrouded in white cloth, which stretch for acres in a flattened perspective as if piled one on top of the other. Like a bad moment in town-planning when the need for a main road got overlooked, there is no discernable path through, no access, no route. I try to read a label or two but it's impossible. Lord Somebody enquires what that particularly long shape over there with the poky up bit is and Corin/Dave asserts that it is in fact a canoe. Is the irony lost on everyone but me? Remi, still surrounded by patrons, is chewing his beard.

An elderly, distinguished looking woman, with bifocals and an expensive haircut, nudges me in the ribs.

"Really, I do think they should be concentrating more on their ethnographic remit rather than all this money spent on natural history, don't you?" she says, searching my face with a myopic yet beady stare.

I shift a little away from her bony elbows, not knowing how to reply. If I disagree, I may seem rude. If I concur, I'm being disloyal to Remi.

"Of course," she continues, "it's chauvinistic euro-centrism. And a lousy education system. Teachers don't know fuck all about culture." I can hear the east London twang under her posh tones now.

"Maybe children prefer learning about animals rather than statues?" I suggest.

"There's no rigour anymore," she gestures to the room of shrouds. "When my husband and I were guests of the Maharajah of Jaipur..."

We are interrupted by Corin and Dave's boss, who is herding us all into the freezer room to discuss the dangers of importing ethnographically varied insects into the building which, if unchecked, will destroy the museum from within.

Centuries later, we emerge to find a pretty, young woman waiting to guide us to the textile department. Corin and Dave explain they have to go now, one to conduct an advanced workshop on pest-control for the museum staff and the other to continue cataloguing his drawers.

Lord Somebody falls into step with the pretty, young woman at the front. Remi is caught up in conversation with Corin and Dave's boss just behind them. The other elderly patrons are milling around each other in the centre, leaving my new friend, Edwina, and me to provide the tail of this many-headed, multi-limbed creature. Luckily there is a lift, and the elderly patrons shuffle in with a collective sigh of gratitude.

The textile room is equally disappointing; no sumptuous wall hangings but racks and racks of long rolls of who knows what, wrapped in white, protective covering and therefore all looking identical. The pretty, young woman gives a slow, ponderous explanation of the many stages of preserving cloth.

Edwina digs me in the ribs again.

"Funny they have a girl showing us the fabric, don't you think?" she says in a stage whisper. "Coincidence or blatant sexism?"

"What was her name?" I reply, really quietly. "I've forgotten it already."

"Martha? Moira? Hah! It's immaterial." She cackles at her own joke, causing Lord Somebody to frown at us both.

The final stop on our journey is the room of bits and pieces, the runt of the litter. As I enter I see before me a wall of swords. Now I'm excited. Or rather, I would be if they were not all swaddled in plastic and stacked in horizontal rows reaching up to the ceiling.

I read the label on the nearest one, 'Japan. 14th century.' How I'd love to hold it, stroke it, smell it.

"When my husband and I were guests of the Maharajah of Jaipur..." Edwina has taken the floor, "... he presented us with a pair of hunting swords, slightly curved you know. They were above the fireplace but the grandchildren kept trying to get them off the wall so I've put them away. Perhaps the museum would like to have them?"

"No!" I cry inwardly. "Edwina, are you mad!"

Lord Somebody looks first at the pretty, young woman and then at Corin and Dave's boss, who both respond with a similar lack of excitement. Remi looks at his watch, and the elderly patrons um and ah and possibly wonder what they might have at home of a similarly exotic nature.

"He had sixty five children by the way," Edwina continues, unperturbed by the lacklustre reaction to her offer and, obviously, unable to hear my silent screams. "Quite a dynasty."

The pretty, young woman opens a drawer, slowly puts on a pair of white gloves and, even more slowly, takes out a pair of chopsticks. At last, a treasure in the flesh. I can see colour – and texture – and design.

"Eighteenth century," she says. A traveller's set of implements carved from bone with jade handles, well worn as if bearing the imprint of the owner's hands. Marvellous. But even this is not enough to lure me from my disappointment. I almost feel as if I've been brought here under false pretences. What was it Remi said? A chance to see all the stuff the public never gets to look at. Serves me right for trying to be elitist, I suppose.

"Hello, darling," Remi is suddenly at my side and puts his arm round me in a propriertorial way. "Having fun?"

"Oh yes," I enthuse, remembering why I am here. "Fascinating, darling."

Edwina leans across me and pinches Remi's sleeve.

"Are you a vivisectionist?" she growls.

"Oh no," Remi laughs, baring his fine, white teeth for a moment, "I'm only interested in animals that are at least a hundred years old."

"Well, then," Edwina says, "as that includes most of us lot..." She gestures to the elderly patrons all crowded round the chopsticks, "... are we to assume we are not safe from your knife?"

"Perfectly safe," Remi says. "You've only got two legs."

Calcium Carbonate was first made as a homeopathic remedy by Samuel Hahnemann from the inside of an oyster shell. The oyster has a hard exterior, a soft, fleshy middle and a pearl at its centre. Like an underground museum storehouse, it sits on the sea bed and guards its treasure.

Calcium's main role is to provide structure. It is a primary substance. Although found most plentifully in the shells of molluscs and birds eggs, both of which provide a container for soft, squishy stuff, it is required to form and maintain skeletons – the structure of vertebrates having moved, through evolution, from an outer shell to an inner framework.

Calcium is found in chalk, limestone and marble and is used in the building industry to make cement and builders' lime.

In the human body, calcium is metabolised in the thyroid gland and the typical symptoms of an under-functioning thyroid; slowness, weight gain and lack of energy, are remarkably similar to the homeopathic remedy picture of Calcium Carbonate (Calc Carb). This is of a somewhat inert being with a placid disposition, content to move slowly through the world or not move at all. Like the middle of the oyster, the Calc Carb patient is flabby, fleshy and cold. The early materia medicas speak of a fair-haired, pale skinned type, though this picture was formed by European homeopaths who rarely, if ever, encountered patients from Asia, Africa or the Caribbean, and may have been an attempt to draw a parallel between human physical characteristics and the whiteness calcium gives to chalk, milk, bone, and teeth.

The fat, placid Calc Carb baby, though a joy to be with because she is so undemanding, may have delayed dentition and be slow to walk, both high calcium processes, and as she grows become fearful and obstinate when coping with any kind of change.

The adult Calc Carb is a dutiful plodder, preferring routine and the safety of an organised structure to the excitement of the unknown, and can be prone either to lethargy or to over-burdening herself with responsibilities. Feeling weighed down by her duties and her slow metabolism, the over-burdened Calc Carb may become increasingly unable to cope and fearing this will be detected by those around her retreats further into her shell, removing herself from view. Like a bureaucracy or a museum warehouse too full of stuff, Calc Carb, through exaggerated diligence, succumbs to overload; the system becomes clogged and slowly breaks down.

Inactivity causes bone loss and the elders of the species are as much in need of calcium as the newcomers. Osteoporosis is more to do with lifestyle than an inevitable symptom of ageing – astronauts lose bone density in space.

The ability of science to extract DNA from skeletons of long dead creatures, some, such as the woolly mammoth dating back 30,000 years, suggests that the bones contain the authentic physical self. Stripped of the layers of muscle and flesh and unadorned by the layers of behaviour, the skeleton gives the real picture of the individual, an enduring truth.

Ancient marine invertebrates can also be studied in this way, to reconstruct the history of shifts in climate and ocean flow, their shells like indelible ink writing the story of the planet through calcium.

"Well, let's hope we never have to come here again," Remi says as we walk to the tube, the wind now at our backs, the landscape still soothingly uncluttered.

Edwina had cadged a lift from a pair of elderly patrons, and was off with barely a wave; Lord Somebody was met by a Bentley; Corin and Dave's boss, after having thanked everyone profusely for attending and put in a plea for more funds, invited Remi and me to the pub. It turns out that Corin and Dave's boss is actually the museum's one-man fundraising department, and is so broke himself he's moonlighting for a PR firm in the City. He confessed all this over scampi and chips. His name is Frank, which almost caused me to snort tartare sauce everywhere.

I look sideways at Remi, his dark skin almost ashen from the wind.

"But won't you have to be paraded at endless boring functions designed to part benefactors from their pots of gold?" I enquire, sneezing from the draught going down the back of my neck.

"Probably," Remi says. "Are you cold?"

"Not at all, darling. I think I just have an allergy to plunder," I manage to say before I sneeze again.

"Oh really, darling." He gives me his handkerchief. "Ah, the nineteenth century. Think about this: at the same time as the philosophers were bickering among themselves about the meaning of history, the philanthropists were amassing artefacts from the colonies and building museums, constructing their own historical fancies, in order to educate the common people back home."[14]

"Sounds like you've got the bare bones of a theory there," I say, my nose now running profusely.

"Only a skeleton so far. I'm having trouble fleshing out my argument," he says, pulling his collar up around his ears.

"I take it you're referring to European philosophers?"

"Of course. Is there any other kind?"

"That's hilarious coming from a Muslim."

He grins at me. "Corin gave me his number. Suggested we meet later in the week for a drink."

"Outed already? Guess my performance wasn't up to scratch, then."

"No," he rubs my back as I sneeze again, "you did great. It's a body language thing."

We reach the station, a faux marble tribute to modernity, and Remi stops to buy a paper while I shiver in the forecourt. Oh no, I realise, we're going underground again, to move like creatures of the deep through dark tunnels of an evolutionary journey.

---

14 Remi had been reading John Gray's 'Straw Dogs' on the train.

I fish in my pockets for my Oyster card and find the camera and notebook I'd stashed so many hours before.

As I flick through the notebook's empty pages, Remi points to the electronic indicator overhead which says that, due to a broken-down engine on the line, our train has been delayed. It doesn't matter. We've got The Guardian crossword to do, perhaps a better use of my detective skills, and, although our passage through space has been temporarily halted, we have right now, in this moment, I think, all the time in the world.

The Homeopath Is NOT In

From my bedroom window I can see blue, cloudless sky but I don't care. Horrible beams of wintry sunlight invade my eyes and my head starts to pound again. Turning away from the window provokes another coughing fit, which makes my skull feels as if this time it really will shatter into my lungs, and my eyeballs scream. I lay back exhausted, convinced I will never enjoy a sunny day again as the shattering subsides and the sweating begins.

Remi arrives with a large dish of lasagne covered in foil, which glints malevolently.

"Oh, I thought you were going to make potato soup," I whisper.

"Nobody likes potato soup," he scoffs. "It's boring. Have you phoned the doctor yet?"

"I've got flu. I don't need a doctor to tell me that."

"It's probably pneumonia," he says. "I think you're being totally irresponsible."

My aunt, Erica, who lives in Clapham and is a retired cardiologist, comes by with tomato soup heavily laced with garlic. The smell makes me want to vomit.

"I've put lots of garlic in it because that's good for you."

"Thanks."

The phone rings. Erica answers it. It's Remi. Erica bristles. They've met before at one of my parties and didn't get on. They argued about string theory, I think. I creep under the covers.

"I'm perfectly aware that she's got pneumonia and I have everything under control, thank you," Erica says.

My head starts to do this creaky, hinge-swinging thing and I try not to cough.

"Yes, she is stubborn but... well, I'm right here and you're...where did you say you were?... Tunbridge Wells? Exactly."

She hangs up.

"Your... friend and I both agree with each other," she says.

I'm tempted to tell her that that 'both' is superfluous, grammatically incorrect, tautological. It causes me a physical pain, that 'both', somewhere in the region of my lower back.

"Can I have a hot water bottle, please?" I ask, peeking from behind my duvet wall. A gorgon of my genealogy, Erica looks me straight in the eye – yet instead of turning to stone I feel myself dissolving into a heap of granulated husks, winnowed by the fierce grip of her displeasure.

Tyrone wanders in. He's just back from his dad's, having taken clean clothes for Ricky who, thankfully, has been looked after there since I got ill.

Erica almost leaps on him.

"Tyrone, I am, as you well know, a heart specialist with a comprehensive medical training and many years of invaluable experience. In my opinion, your mother needs to go to hospital for a chest x-ray. I am going to give you the telephone number of Seldoc and you must phone them now – if you don't want her leaving the house in a box, that is."

Tyrone looks terrified. I shake my head and attempt a wink through gummy eyelids while Erica, distracted, searches in her bag for a pen.

"Righto," he says and quietly backs out of the room.

"I don't want a doctor," I say to Erica. "I really have no use for a doctor. I don't have pneumonia. I have flu."

I stop there, exhausted.

She paces heavily round the room, then looks at her watch.

"I have to go. I'm late for Pilates. Tyrone can at least heat up the soup for you. I'm going to phone Seldoc myself. Obviously I can't trust anyone else. My sciatica's killing me and my nerves are..."

I groan, and try to look as wan as possible.

"... and anyway... you just get better."

She kisses me so hard on my cheek, I fear the bone may splinter.

Hurtling off down the stairs, she calls Tyrone. I don't bother to strain to hear a murmured discussion between them in the hall because my ears have suddenly filled up with something which may be porridge or wallpaper paste but is probably catarrh. I find I can barely hear at all. What a good idea. Still no hot water bottle though. Still no potato soup.

I dream of a 12ft Angelina Jolie whose long limbs turn into the legs of an old striped deckchair. Chinese warriors gallop through narrow mountain arteries to reinforce my immune system; each one of their swords like a spark of chi, their hoof beats thundering against my ribs.

"Counter-attack," one of them urges, but I can't remember any of the moves.

There is a frantic call from the children's father. Ricky has got a fever and needs his mum.

He arrives, flushed, hot and vomiting. Tyrone gives him Belladonna and puts him into bed with me where he thrashes all night, mumbling in some exotic language of his own. Belladonna by the hour and next morning he is peaceful and no longer too hot, while I am regressing to an amoebic state – like a sandy footprint whose form has no substance but is held together by pressure and is helpless against the incoming tide.

Scarlett Johansson appears in an enormous scarlet dress. Crass, I think, while trying to unzip it for her and help her into an equally oversized white robe. She sneezes into the mirror in the old curiousity shop we seem to be in. Oh no, that was me who sneezed. The vibration rumbles violently through the mattress.

No longer amoebic, I lie scattered again among the saturated sheets while I try to figure out a way to look after a seven year old and then give up with a desperate little laugh of defeat. Scarlett digs her scarlet nails into my eyes as I fall through a rabbit hole into another tormented fissure of sleep.

Beatrice, the manager of the community centre where I work, phones to check my progress. I'm aware that the postponed appointments are stacking up. She asks me what remedies my homeopath has prescribed. I feel all my blood draining away.

"I... I haven't got round to phoning her yet."

"You what?!"

"To be honest, I forgot I had a homeopath. I've been... all over the place."

There is no snappy resentment in Beatrice's voice. It seems that she is not pissed off with me for being ill, despite the backlog. She gets me to agree to make the call.

Before I can do so, the phone rings again. It's Seldoc, who have had a message that someone at this number needs urgent medical assistance. I flush with anger whilst trying to sound cool rather than shivery.

Running efficiently through my list of symptoms, the doctor on the other end of the phone says I've probably got flu and given that I'm a homeopath she's quite happy for me to carry on taking whatever. I feel safe for a moment, less unhinged. I call Sandy, my homeopath, who is of course not answering. I leave a pathetic message and, having hung up, try and recall all the remedies I have given myself in the past several days. Finding only loss of memory where the list should be, I fall back into a snivelling pool of mucus and then cough for several explosive minutes until the top of my head flies off and a flock of demented starlings swoops from inside my skull into the rank night air.

Ricky bounces back to his dad's and Tyrone collapses. He spends a day in his own room then moves his couch into my bedroom, (can't be that ill, I think, if he can lift a couch), and we languish together, listening to Radio Four and discussing big subjects like racism and feminism in a woozy, dreamlike way without a single argument. Time hangs in a hammock above us as we wake each day to another several hours of doing nothing.

Sandy calls back and is most interested in my delusions of giant female Hollywood film stars. She tells me to take Stannum, followed by Silica. Stannum is made from tin and is indicated for a cough with extreme weakness. As I take the remedy, I picture myself in a sunny Cornish tin mine wearing a hard hat and... I'm liking the sun again. I'm standing in the sun, taking Stannum.

Marjorie comes from next door to cleanse the space.

"I told yer to watch out for your adrenals. I could see this comin," she says, lighting a stick of sage and setting little fires of lavender and eucalyptus. I think she's put one under the bed, which makes me slightly nervous, but it's generally very pleasant and uplifting. Then I've suddenly had enough and tell her that I need to sleep. She looks at Tyrone on his couch next to me, who has snored through the entire ceremony.

"Bless' im," she murmurs and blows everything out so that it gets a bit smoky and I start coughing.

When the smoke clears she's still sitting on the end of the bed. I ask her if she knows how to make potato soup.

"Does it contain chilli?"

"No."

"Then I can't say that I do."

Tina, on tour in the provinces, calls me with the news that she got a standing ovation for her Cordelia last night. I'm thrilled of course but a bit miffed that, in her excitement, she neglects to ask me how I am. Then I remember she's a bit miffed that I'm not getting on a train to watch her.

Beatrice visits with potato soup made to my specifications – just potato and a bit of stock. She's a woman, and my boss, but I want to marry her. Tyrone says he'll stick to dry toast and oranges, thanks. We're both so thin now, we look like stick people. I draw a cartoon of Tyrone and Me In Bed

With Flu. Tyrone's hair is on fire and I am peeking from behind a rock.

"You are perilously in want of grooming," my mother's voice says in a kind of geometric soundscape, which floods the ceiling and cascades around the walls. I try to remember the whereabouts of my hairbrush but then the thought of anything touching my scalp gives me an almost unbearable rush of goose bumps so I try and make the ceiling go away instead.

Max, who can't walk let alone cook, sends several cartons of supermarket soup by delivery for me to sample. How did he know? I'm so touched, but the desire to phone and talk to him is missing. I text instead. He texts back that we had a long phone conversation a few days ago about soup, and the difference between truth, honesty, authenticity and fact. I have no recollection of this either.

Like a crystal hanging in a dark cave, my consciousness seems to hover in space yet, at the same time, keeps attempting to reorganise my form and structure, with accompanying inappropriate emotional motifs, whilst daily fevers undo all the work and, like Sisyphus, I keep rolling the rock back up the hill.

Camille sends a Fortnum and Mason hamper by courier. Tyrone perks up immediately and phones his friends, who all come round for dinner and wreck the kitchen. But I have no fury. That would require energy. I phone Aunt Erica, who sends me Carmela.

Carmela has a deportation order hanging over her and has been hiding out at Erica's, trying to find something useful to do in a house that is already immaculate. She is hungry for a distraction. Tyrone takes her to pick Ricky up from school and my little one, once re-instated, gives me a brief hug then bossily instructs Carmela as to the best way to make a fish-finger sandwich. Tyrone, back on the couch after his exertions, says he's almost not looking forward to being well enough to get permanently off the couch.

I tell him I know just what he means and we realise at the same time that we've created one of those family stories "Do you remember the time when..."

Carmela brings the rocking chair from Ricky's room to sit in. I give her the tube of hand-cream by my bed and she squirts a big dollop and massages her fingers, palms, and wrists with gusto. She tells me about her recent run-in with the Home Office; her two children back home who she hasn't seen for fifteen years; her husband's murder by the government forces; the fact that she is actually on the run, a fugitive by virtue of having been married to a guerrilla freedom-fighter, and that there is a price on her head. This is so horribly fascinating I forget to cough, sneeze, groan or sweat for several minutes. Carmela is beautiful and kind. Her earrings glint a bit too brightly for my sore eyes but otherwise she is sparkly in all the right places, despite so much tragedy. She tells me that Erica has probably saved her life and that she knows I must be a good person by association.

"Nice family," she says, nodding. "Nice family."

I start to feel a buzz of energy, a faint murmur of assent through my scattered systems. They want to cooperate again. There's a world of pain and injustice to attend to. Somehow, I've got to rejoin the fray.

Remi sends me a quote from Bertrand Russell by text.

"Mathematics may be defined as the subject in which we never know what we are talking about, nor whether what we are saying is true."[15]

Remi adds that Tyrone might find this helpful for his maths A level.

"Here's the good news." I hand Tyrone the phone.

He reads the text, then puts the phone down and pretends to faint.

"Guess who I am," he says, squinting up at me from a dangly off-the-couch position, a hand resting limply on his brow.

"Er... Bertrand Russell?"

"Nope."

"Remi?"

"Nope."

"Ricky, after too much chocolate? Me, generally? Aunt Erica in need of a doctor?"

"Nope."

"I give up."

"Head of the World Bank innit. Busted!"

My cough having subsided, and therefore my head feeling more intact, my eyeballs less under assault, I've stopped taking Stannum and am now on the Silica.

Silica is the second most common constituent of the earth's crust, exceeded only by oxygen. It is found largely as silicon oxides such as sand, quartz and rock crystal. This

15 Bertrand Russell - Recent Work on the Principles of Mathematics, published in International Monthly, vol. 4 (1901) .

gives a clue to the structural role it plays as a homeopathic remedy.

The classic homeopathic texts describe Silica's remedial power as being the answer to a 'want of grit.' I always think of John Wayne when I hear this phrase and see him swaggering across a dusty plain, both hands poised over the holsters at his sides, ready for anything. This is the complete antithesis of the Silica state, in which the person has lost the swagger and become more like the dust – the holster is empty, the bullets are spent.

In the acute situation, this lack of stamina is often brought about by overwork, a shortage of sleep, missed meals and other prosaic forms of self-neglect. The robust, healthy person can overdraw on Silica reserves if the energy bank account is not kept robustly, healthily in credit. The maths stops adding up, the flashing minus signs are ignored and, like a collapsing economy, the fall can be swift. Yet within the collapse there is a heightened sensitivity to external stimuli as if the usual boundaries have been dissolved. The senses are 'morbidly keen.'[16]

Alternatively, Silica can be used towards the lingering end of an illness slow to resolve, when the chaos has subsided and the deficit can be defined in clearer terms.

Silica is expulsive, bringing to the surface any lurking toxins. It can remove splinters and other foreign bodies and for this reason it cannot be used with patients who have had joint replacements or pacemakers.

The Silica constitutional type is fine, like sand or crystal, shy, sensitive and as delicate as glass. However, like glass, she can be transparent yet rigid. Stubborn in a non-argu-

16 E.A.Farrington – Clinical Materia Medica: B.Jain Publishers PVT Ltd, reissued 2010

mentative way, and resistant to changing her views, her strength of will is in contrast to the tendency to weakness on the physical plane.

The invention of the glass-fibre optic and the silicon chip have revolutionised the form and structure of mass communication. The quartz crystal has harnessed time. The clarity of crystal symbolises the nature of Silica's mental acumen and perceptive power. The intellect is shrewd, the mind is clear and yet, when ill, the same mind can become prey to delusions. James Tyler Kent who, after Hahnemann, is the foremost historical homeopath described the Silica patient's intellectual struggle as if '... he feels his own selfhood and cannot enter into his subject.'[17]

In the night, as the Silica deposits itself in my energy bank account, I hear murmurs, fragmentary sentences...

"... between the crystal and the drain ... the sum of the squares on the opposite two sides ... erring on the good side of wrong ... maybe only the stones understood ... quite the storyteller, aren't you ... it was a non-functioning way of going about things ... don't try this at home..."

The spiky shards of my fever, still whispering faintly, have less and less to engage with as my strength returns. The screen goddesses are recalled to L.A. The Chinese warriors have unbridled their horses, which are now grazing peacefully on a terraced hill. As I wonder how they manage to balance on the slope, I feel my own limbs stretch into alignment. The night is no longer dangerous or distorted. The voices recede.

17 James Tyler Kent – Lectures on Homeopathic Materia Medica: B.Jain Publishing Pvt.Ltd, reissued 2002

My bedroom is crowded with furniture – Tyrone's couch, Ricky's rocking chair. Carmela's left her earrings on the chest of drawers and Marjorie has brought over a bag full of crystals which are arranged around the room in a feng shui pattern that only Marjorie understands. I'll ask her to come and do some more space clearing I think. Get Tyrone's couch and Ricky's chair back where they belong. Get some order round here.

Tomorrow I may feel well enough to get dressed, find my hairbrush, find my diary, even make potato soup myself – although, now that I'm well enough, I may find I don't really want or need it anymore. I may require more than soup to get me going. I may develop an appetite for something stronger.

Enlighten This

'Bhikkhus, all is burning.'
Buddha – The Fire Sutra

Camden is not my territory and, like any self-respecting South Londoner, I suffer from an ancient prejudice when having to travel further north than Oxford Street. Although crossing the river that runs through our city is always a joy, I prefer to stay within walking distance of it when on the other side.

North Londoners have an even greater distaste for Thames hopping. They think the city ends at the river and whatever lies beyond the South Bank should be avoided at all costs. It's just the way it is.

However, as my history includes a brief spell in a ground floor flat on Camden Road in the early 1980s, I am not a complete stranger to these parts and locate my final destination without a map.

On the train, I was reading a book about the siege of Malta and nearly missed my stop. This World War Two bombardment of my father's home was the second siege, the first having taken place in the 16th century. In the first case the goal of the enemy, Suleiman the Magnificent, was to gain a route from east to west and spread Islam to the heart of Catholic Europe and, in the second, the Italians were trying to secure a line from west to east to shore up the Nazis' North African campaign. In both cases, Malta was in the way. The relentless hammering of this tiny island should have meant an easy victory for the would-be conquerors but, in both cases, the tenacity and bravery of the Maltese withstood the onslaught and Malta did not fall. This was pivotal in wrecking the expansionist plans of the enemy. Without Malta, life in Europe may have been very different

I find myself welling up at the thought of all the heroic deeds that were committed by ordinary mortals as well as dashing fighter pilots and my distant ancestors, the Knights of St John, and wonder if the fact that Malta has been invaded by practically everyone else during its long history, when things weren't quite so crucial, has given the Maltese people strength through inter-racial tolerance. My legs are shaky as I leap out of the train at the last minute.

I, too, feel under siege today. The campaign against homeopathy rages and, having started to dread receiving yet another email concerning the bullying tactics of our enemies or the attempts by our profession to limit the damage, let alone listening to regular bursts of anti-homeopathy propaganda on Radio Four (a bit like suffering betrayal from an old friend), I have come to Camden for a seminar and group discussion hosted by an outfit which has the reputation of being at the cutting edge of contemporary spiritual consciousness. If the sharpness of their suits is anything to go by, a corporate look that immediately makes me feel uneasy, I'd better keep on my toes – perhaps even when sitting down. As long as they don't try to sell me something.

In the queue for registration, I'm accosted by two German women who admire my handbag. They are editors of an enlightening magazine in Zurich and look like they have several Swiss bank accounts between them. We walk together through the reception into what appears to be a palace and climb the stairs to the conference suite via a four-story atrium which sheds a column of hard, cold light onto the milling figures below.

The place is packed and as people spill out of the lift at the top a bottleneck forms, reducing the space to a claustrophobic tunnel. The two Germans have disappeared, so I avoid making eye contact with anyone else for the time being and just look for a seat.

After a morning spent getting to know each other during which, when it's my turn, I confess that I have come today seeking like-minded people but am not sure what that means, I am eager for lunch and zoom down to the cafeteria ahead of the crowd. Piling my plate with bespoke vegan delicacies, I sit at an empty table that becomes full very quickly with various individuals who, instead of carrying on their own little conversations, establish a group debate on the proceedings so far. I'm expected to join in and somehow get into an argument with a young man called Will who, it transpires, is the son of James, the organization's director and our seminar leader for the day. Will, although wearing trainers and a hoodie, is keen to expound the party line, which has an impeccable lineage but doesn't sound so great coming from him. His arrogance is understandable given his age, about twenty two, but I don't like being patronized so I forget about keeping on my toes and jump.

"If you are of the opinion that everybody's opinion is equally valid," I say, "what happens if I am of the opinion that your opinion sucks?"

He looks startled.

"Am I still included in the debate? If I am a fascist dictator or fundamentalist Muslim cleric, is my opinion still valid? Do you let me in?"

I gaze at the absurdity of my desires while trying to stop my knee from jerking. Will recovers and says, "Enlightened debate is the cornerstone of our emerging spiritual evolution."

"Can a cornerstone evolve?" I reply. "I would have thought that, by definition, the opposite was true."

"You're missing the point," he says, as if I'm stupid to be doing so.

It's ridiculous to be wrangling like this, given that we're on the same side. This is not how wars are won. My inner terrorist fails to agree and urges me to lob a few more missiles Will's way.

"My inner terrorist," I say, "thinks that the only point is the pin of a grenade. Being right is actually impossible, so why are we pretending we have an answer? Why are we here, really?"

Unfortunately, most of the other people at the table overhear this exchange and Will gives up trying to get me to behave and turns away without answering, I have a feeling he'll be gunning for me later. I can't even remember who started the skirmish now and, as the vegan delicacies start to react with my gastric juices, I try to remember the location of the loos instead. Damn, I'm going to have to ask.

"Can someone enlighten me as to the whereabouts of the Ladies?" I say to the group, all of whom, I now realise by their lack of response, are friends of Will's.

"I need to go too. Let's look together," says a beautiful woman I hadn't noticed before. Like an angel, she has appeared at my side and is already pulling back my chair for me.

"I can't believe you tried to assassinate the crown prince," she giggles as we walk towards the stairs. "I'm Lucia, by the way. Ciao."

She holds out a slender hand.

"Neither can I," I say. "Probably not my cleverest move."

What I really want to say is "And where were you at the time? Thanks for the back-up," but I am already entranced by her warm handshake, her long black hair, her sparkling eyes and her shimmering smile.

In the afternoon session we are split into groups and I make sure Lucia and I are in the same one. She's an art teacher from Perugia, discovered homeopathy when her children were small and has been using it ever since. She had no idea that we were suffering such merciless attacks in the U.K. Like many of my patients, she takes no notice of the negative reports in the mainstream media as she knows homeopathy works. How it works doesn't interest her. She's been coming here for quite a while to meditate and study, and seems to be friends with everyone. This makes her gesture of alliance a little suspect.

Will is on the other side of the room. That's good. His father, James, is beaming at everyone, me included, so that's good too.

We spend two hours doing consciousness-raising exercises that leave me woolly-headed, and with a load more awkward questions. Planning to avoid Will, I don't rush down to the cafeteria when it's time for a break but stay in the conference room with several others, including Lucia, who invites me to share her big bottle of sparkling mineral water. The suits hover, listening in to the chat.

I'm dreading the final session, the whole group coming together again to share our experiences of the day, as I know I won't be able to lie and I'm frantically looking for a good excuse to leave now. Lucia notices my discomfort and offers to massage my shoulders. Surrendering to her light yet convincing touch, I think of the Maltese and try and summon some staying power.

Phosphorous means bringer of light and the phosphorous bombs used by both sides in World War Two certainly looked pretty on their way down, sparkling like fireworks in the dark. A deadly poison, causing horrific burns and eating through bone, phosphorous is one of the nastier ingredients in the chemist's manual of modern warfare. When exposed to air, it combusts and burns with a cold flame.

Although it is illegal to use chemical weapons against civilian targets, phosphorous bombs have continued to be deployed by the U.S. Israel, Saudi Arabia and Iraq in several more recent major conflicts, causing collateral damage of a terrible kind. Phosphorous was added to napalm during the Vietnam War, to make it burn better, and has been linked to Gulf War Syndrome.

Phosphorous is also a component of DNA and is an essential constituent in our diet, occurring naturally as phosphates in many foods. However, the prolific use of organo-phosphates in fertilizers and pesticides has changed the nature of the soil on which we depend. Phosphates in detergents have increased the phosphorous content of our lakes and rivers, and are responsible for the blooming of toxic algae. Organo-phosphates have been linked to excessive tiredness, headaches, limb pains, disturbed sleep, poor concentration, mood changes, and suicidal impulses.

The effects of phosphorous poisoning make it one of the major remedies in the homeopathic materia medica. It has an affinity with all the body systems and its main uses are in diseases of the lungs, bones, liver and nerves. However, the physical complaints which may respond to the remedy, Phosphorous, differ in their variety from the distinct, explicit constitutional type.

Slim and beautiful, with luxuriant hair, captivating eyes and a lively, affectionate personality, Phosphorous, with an openhearted grace, will easily make you feel the spark of kinship and, like the striking of a match in the darkness, illuminate your world. However, this is a creature of the air whose sensitivity to the atmosphere can quickly exhaust her and whose light, though dependent on the reflection of others, will too readily absorb any negativity around her and become more deeply affected than most by suffering, sadness and cruelty. In times of trouble, the empathetic Phosphorous will always seek to be the peacemaker and to bring succour to the underdog. Easily influenced, she will become ill through taking on the suffering of others as if it was her own.

Although many remedies share a worsening of symptoms at night, Phosphorous is aggravated at twilight, when the boundaries are indistinct and the light diffuse. The fears are many and to be alone is a form of torture. Phosphorous can only feel substantial when relating, as the ethereal quality of her untethered existence can cause her to feel as tenuous as a brief flame. This makes her extremely vulnerable to criticism and to being ignored.

If her luminescence fails to be admired, Phosphorous can reveal a darker side. Cruelty and revenge emerge from beneath the superficial warmth that has failed to entice and enchant, relationships are callously tossed aside and, like a bombing raid, the cold flame can turn pathological.

The Phosphorous patient craves ice cream, chocolate and fizzy drinks and is particularly sensitive to cold air which brings on sore throats and chest infections. Collapse can be sudden, but the patient will invariably feel better for company, physical contact and reassurance. The materia medicas talk of the desire to be 'magnetized' and, like a cat, Phosphorous will purr with pleasure when being stroked.

James takes his place in the large circle we have formed for the debrief, looks straight at me and muses on the disease of 'Already Knowing.' As he talks about the ego's struggle to maintain separation at all costs in order not to be subsumed by the glorious and enlightening practice of connecting with the energy of the universe, encompassing all beings, I understand that my habitual role of awkward questioner is an attempt on my part to not lose sight of who I am. I feel humbled for a moment, then my inner terrorist starts enumerating all the certainties I've heard during the day which, by their apparent veracity, exclude several million beings from the group.

Lucia, next to me, is nodding at his words and I regret that I can't just nod along with her. Is my sense of self that important?

"I'd just like to say," I say, when there's a bit of a gap in the general feelgood backslapping, "that, although I really appreciate what you're doing here, I've spent the whole day pretty much wanting to leave. I feel uncomfortable with your terminology and I question whether such an intellectual approach to spiritual practice isn't just a capitulation to the prevailing forces, like shooting yourself in the foot, or bombing your own side."

"Excellent," says James, beaming profusely at me, "I think that's the first really true statement anyone has made all afternoon. Congratulations for not leaving."

As I fall in love with James who, dash it all, is married with a 22 year old son, Lucia, who is sitting next to me, pats my arm. I feel myself welling up again as I look at the faces of all these seekers of enlightenment around me. These are some of the people who are actively trying to change the face of what's possible and to bring illumination into a world of shadows. How irritating that I feel I just don't fit. Will is writing something in a little notebook on his lap.

Outside at last, I pause under the light in the porch of the building and breathe in the cold night air. A young man stands a little way off trying to light a cigarette and, when he sees me, waves and then saunters over.

"Phew," he says, putting his cigarette behind his ear and his matches in his coat pocket. "Were you in there too?"

"I think so," I reply.

He laughs.

"Why are you here?" I ask.

"Oh… networking." He puts his hand back in his pocket, pulls out a business card and gives it to me. On the front, in psychedelic lettering, it says 'We Are One'. I turn it over and read 'A party about loving life' and then his name, Dan Lightfoot, and a South London address.

"SE19? Where's that?" I ask, "Forest Hill?"

"Close. I put on raves in Crystal Palace. All-nighters. You should come."

"Really? Thanks." I'm flattered that he thinks I look young enough.

"And you?" he asks. "What's your excuse?"

I think of the war against homeopathy and the part I'm being forced to play in the conflict; my lack of desire to take sides, and the inevitability of being drawn into something that requires an identification, a tribal badge that goes against all my instincts.

"Boredom," I reply.

The two German women emerge from the building into the cold. Wrapped in fur, they smile briefly, as if recognizing me from some other time, and walk off into the night.

"Do you rave in Camden, too?" I ask Dan.

"Not likely," he replies. "If I'm honest, North London creeps me out a bit. And the rents are ridiculous."

I say goodbye to Dan and wend my way down Camden Road. I'll give his card to Tina, who may even know him already, the South London event scene being terribly cliquey. Tina, my phosphoric child who, when little, used to apologise to inanimate objects when bumping into them; who would hide under the bed during a thunderstorm; who always wanted chocolate when unwell and who can't bear to watch the scary movies that her friends love so much, has just texted me from home.

She's looking for the fairy lights to hang at the sitting-room window. She's fed up with the dark and thinks we need a boost, a 'fillip' she writes, as we head towards the solstice and the long hours of night.

"They're in the attic," I text back, "with the Christmas decorations."

Where else would the light be but nestling in the darkness? Electric stars waiting to be connected to the circuit, to be plugged in to the juice – symbols of hope, wonder, peace on earth and goodwill to all.

Shut Up And Talk

The week before Christmas and it's raining hard. There are boys all over the house. Tyrone, plus four of his extremely adolescent compadres, and Ricky, who is, to his disgust, still only seven. The teenagers loll on various bits of furniture toying with various bits of electronic equipment, guffawing at each other's fart jokes, grunting and spilling things on the floor. Ricky whines constantly to be allowed to have a go on something, anything, and keeps kicking his brother, who retaliates by periodically banishing him to the hall so that he can keep kicking the door instead.

Meanwhile, Tina is holding court round the kettle with two of her girlfriends. Yes, they will be staying for dinner, thank you. No, they don't speak to smelly boys who are younger than them and who are hogging the TV, which just isn't fair, Mum, actually.

Sitting at my kitchen table, immersed in the realm of online paperless billing but with a clear line of vision to the hall, I am outwardly calm, transcending the melee, offering occasional words of comfort to Ricky – who, in demonstrating his preference for negative attention, tells me to mind my own business – and placating Tina's more regal tendencies with a shrug.

With a reverberating thwack, something wet and feline crashes through the cat-flap and, before anyone can do anything, leaps towards me and lands in a very imprecise, un-cat like splat on the keyboard, deleting all my online paperless receipts and, who knows, maybe short-circuiting the entire system with deluge. It's Violet, on the run from the elements. I get an old towel and rub her dry while Tina and her cohorts scream into their mobile phones.

Before I've had a chance to recoup my losses, Jack, our lodger, arrives home with his girlfriend, Suze, who is in urgent need of a shower, a homeopathic remedy and possibly a lawyer, having just slipped on the wet pavement and fallen into an open, muddy trench left behind by Thames Water as part of their modernization programme of the Victorian mains system. I give her Arnica and Rescue Remedy, get Tyrone to make a photographic record of her contusion and, with a hug from the girls, she limps happily upstairs to use all the remaining hot water.

What none of these glorious beings are aware of is that three days ago Carlo and I decided finally, categorically and definitively to call time on our relationship. Not through rancour or disillusion, but prosaically due to living in two different countries with neither of us wanting to move. Despite the loving nature of our break-up, done mostly by email, I howl in the shower daily. It's the only time I can guarantee privacy, although there is often a watchful cat perched on the sink but that doesn't really count. The cats and I share so many secrets – this is just one more. In trying not to expose my grief to my family, to protect them from the news and therefore from my feelings, am I also trying to protect myself? Probably, but then I think, "I'm supposed to be the grown-up of the group. I just have to handle this."

However, the Wise Woman within me, my Inner Crone, knows this is not really an enlightened attitude, more a gritting of teeth.

"You cannot change what you don't acknowledge," she chides. "Enter the feeling and then it will pass quicker. Pain is inevitable, suffering optional."

"You have definitely been reading too many self-help books," I spit back.

"They need to know what's happened," she continues. "It's not a crime to show your sadness. It may help you achieve closure."

"And what if I don't want 'closure'? – how I hate that word. What if I want this gnawing pain to stay stuck at the back of my throat so that I am unable to speak? What if I don't want anyone feeling SORRY FOR ME!!!"

"Ah... I think we've hit a nerve, excellent! You just don't want to show you're vulnerable. But your armour is merely a carapace to cover your back. Your heart is exposed, raw and bleeding. You know it. I know it. Why shouldn't they know it?"

These conversations with myself tire me but I suppose, like Cathy's love for Heathcliff, though 'the source of little visible delight,' they're necessary. I have become uncharacteristically quiet in the past few days, it's true. Rubrics from the homeopathic repertory, 'Ailments from silent grief;' 'Ailments from disappointed love;' float through the static as I go down to the cellar to check on the leak which Carlo tried to fix on his last visit but which always reappears when the heavy rain comes. Water is seeping in through the line between wall and floor. There is a small puddle by the boiler.

Later, I visit a dear friend, Tony, who is dying of cancer. His face has a translucent quality that I've not seen him wear before. He is discarnating rapidly. I hold his hand while he reminisces about surviving a bomb blast in Argentina in the 1970s. His voice is weak and I have to sit very close to hear. But I want to get even closer, jump in the bed with him or strap him down, to hold onto all of him – "Don't go, don't go, don't go."

Rain lashes at the window. I tell him that I've been prescribing remedies for all the characters in Wuthering Heights. He nods, he likes this and, with a sly grin, murmurs that I obviously don't have enough to do. Then he tries to lift his head from the pillow and, as I reach to smooth his hair and settle him back down, he catches hold of my sleeve and, in a dry whisper, asks,

"What are you giving Heathcliff?"

"Hmmm... that depends on which Heathcliff..." I prise his hand open and gently massage his fingers, which are like little twigs now. He has shrunk so much in the last few weeks. "...Boy, man or monomaniac?"

"End-stage."

I almost choke on the provocation and recognise it's a test of nerve. Boys to men to dust. I have to answer, but how? The constriction in my throat and the tension of the past few days, defences against loss, seem suddenly more like falsehoods. I need to speak the truth. Tony closes his eyes, submitting to the pause in our conversation. I'm losing him, and I'm not ready. I could say anything right now, and nothing will change. I plunge further into metaphor, hoping I'm not digging a grave of some sort for myself and wondering how I can even think of myself at all at a time like this.

"Well, um... it isn't clear whether Heathcliff died of starvation or a broken heart. But, whatever... by observing his behaviour at the end, which is all we really have to go on, though bearing in mind it's only second-hand, due to it being a book, and which, if you recall, involved him shutting himself away, retreating into a dark, brooding silence, and... from the aetiology of chronic grief and disappointed love, plus what we know of his tendency towards resentment and dwelling in the past... ghosts notwithstanding... and putting aside the cruelty and violence of the earlier Heathcliff, which of course indicates a different remedy altogether... I think... yes... I think I can safely give him some very high potency Nat Mur and, well... hey... maybe save his life and change the entire course of English literature."

He's drifting off to sleep. I can tell by his breathing that he can't hear me. How many more visits can I fit in before I get the call? Save his life? Or at least save these moments of being close. I remember touching my father's dead face and finding it cold, and that I didn't cry for two years until I discovered homeopathy and learnt how to grieve. I remember Carlo once explaining quantum entanglement to me in order to help me understand that, although we are often separated, we are always connected. The wall around my heart comes crashing down. Grief-encrusted psychic rubble rips through my pores until I feel as if I have no skin.

Nat Mur is the abbreviation of Natrum Muriaticum, otherwise known as sodium chloride or salt. Sodium chloride is an essential constituent of our life on this earth and is responsible for the smooth flow of fluids, both in the sea and in the human body. Without salt, the seas would freeze and the process of osmosis would not be possible. The complex interactions that maintain balance, or homeostasis, in the body are dependant on salt and, therefore, all metabolic functions are affected.

Sodium chloride is found primarily in the fluid that bathes the cells and has a strong affinity for water. The expression, 'Where salt goes, water follows,' is the key.

We always think of Nat Mur as a possible remedy when the patient has symptoms of too much or too little water, when there is either excessive dryness or excessive fluid. Sometimes this polarity is seen in the individual patient who may have, for example, cracked lips and, at the same time, swollen ankles. Salt imbalance often shows up on the skin – too little and it becomes papery dry, too much and it blisters and perspires excessively. An overdose of salt can produce alarmingly toxic effects in the stomach, nervous system, muscles and all the secretory organs. High blood pressure is a common complaint related to salt intake. The materia medicas talk of 'cardiac distress.'

But what does any of this have to do with Heathcliff? And why am I finding this story harder to write than any other? The answers lie, not with the many physical indications for Nat Mur, but with my uncharacteristically silent melancholy – the most common indication for the remedy on the emotional plane.

When we encounter this state in the consulting room, when the patient sits with arms folded and legs crossed, when our questions meet with polite but monosyllabic answers, when the phrase 'blood out of a stone' comes to mind, we think of Nat Mur. Our usual strategies clunk dully against the high walls of the patient's defences. We knock, but are refused. Often, this state is so apparent that, having identified the remedy in the first few minutes, we spend the rest of the consultation trying to discover the reasons for such a reluctance to speak – to locate the unattended lookout post, beyond which we may slip through the barrier of silence.

It may transpire that the patient has either a craving for or an aversion to salt and there may be other satisfyingly confirmatory symptoms of a physical nature. But, underneath the symptoms, there will usually be an inkling of a story to do with loss.

Nat Mur's position at the forefront of the homeopathic repertoire is due to its effectiveness as a remedy for unexpressed grief. The grief is usually connected to loss of a loved one, either through death or an unhappy love affair, and is often of long-standing. Something has disrupted its flow towards resolution and caused it to have a life of its own. The loss, or possibly repeated losses, sometimes dating back to a childhood of being unloved, has produced resentment, a tendency to dwell on past hurts and a grim survival strategy. The Nat Mur patient has resolved never to be hurt again and the only way to ensure this is to never let anyone get close enough to try. There is a tendency to form relationships with no danger of real commitment, such as with someone married or far away yet, paradoxically, there is also a tendency to be the sympathetic ear to whom others turn when distressed. The latter, however, will not be a two-way street. There is no sharing with Nat Mur. The primary experience is one of bitter isolation.

This withholding, this lack of free flow, echoes the fluid imbalance on the material plane. The Nat Mur patient rarely, if ever, cries, and then only when alone. The rubric

'Averse to consolation' joins those of 'silent grief' and 'disappointed love' to form the three-legged stool upon which the patient sits. To give Nat Mur in such cases can bring a wonderful liberation for the patient, if done gently. The homeopath treads a fine line around the dark brooding pain, using the remedy like the call of the wild – an invitation to freedom – which can accomplish in weeks what psychotherapy and other 'talking cures' may take months or even years to achieve.

Nat Mur has been called the 'English' remedy due to our native predilection for the stiff upper lip and dislike of displays of emotion. Also, because we live on an island surrounded by salt water, and haven't been invaded for several centuries.

Reading quotes from the original provings, such as 'Affronts that he had given and received were constantly in his mind'; 'He tormented himself, seemed to prefer disagreeable thoughts' and 'Hatred of people who had insulted him' I can understand Heathcliff in a different light, and wonder if Emily Bronte ever read a book on homeopathy.

Returning home, drenched, I open my inbox. One from Carlo. He says he's having trouble concentrating at work which, given that he is an obstetrician in a busy hospital in Rome, responsible for the safe delivery of hundreds of babies daily, is problematic. He goes on to speculate whether a trip to London may help to clear his head a little. What do I think?

Our quantum entanglement tugs at my heart.

I write 'Yes' and press Send before I can give myself a chance to rationalise my way into doing nothing.

"A woman of few words," observes my Inner Crone. "You still sound a bit Nat Mur if you ask me."

"I didn't ask you," I reply. "I know what's going on. I'm just sorting out the difference between love and attachment."

"You mean it may be finished but it's not over?"

"I mean I'm not going to pin my life down into little compartments with shelves and padlocks, I'm going to let it all just be what it is."

"Right on!" she crows in an annoying mid-Atlantic twang. "My work here is done."

Salt water springs into my eyes, blurring the computer screen and the last remnants of my hard-edged denial. The Crone laughs into her self-improvement manual.

"Do you have anything useful like a Yellow Pages?" I mutter. "I have a leak in my cellar. I need a plumber."

I go into the sitting room, to find Tyrone watching TV with Tina curled up asleep beside him, her head on his shoulder. Ricky is lying face down on a floor cushion, snoring gently.

"Alright, Mum?"

"Bit damp still but, yes, I'm fine. You?"

"Chillin' innit." He grins.

I pick Ricky up and marvel as usual over the length of his eyelashes. Tyrone channel-hops.

"Ty, you know if there's anything bothering you, ever, you just need to say. You do know that, don't you?"

"Mum, I'm fine." He pats Tina's sleeping head. She stirs. "You'd certainly know about it if I weren't."

Resisting the impulse to pursue the subject, I smile. I have taught my children that every feeling has a beginning, a middle and an end, much like a novel. With painful feelings such as grief, it is in the middle, not the end-stage where we can so often get stuck. We bookmark our pain for later, or pretend there is no pain at all. This produces stasis and is contrary to the flow of nature. We can become, like Heathcliff, addicted to our pain so that we will not give it up and are devoured by it, slowly and insidiously from within. Or we can enter the feeling, as the Crone advised, and therefore pass through to the other side.

I carry Ricky upstairs and deposit him into his bed. He sighs, opens his eyes and looks puzzled for a moment before realising where he is and who I am, I kiss his cheek, so soft and warm and alive. I hear Tina and Tyrone bickering on their way upstairs then, somewhere between the bathroom and the landing, they start to giggle.

Tony will be going through his nightly agonies right now. I crawl into bed, hoping that the morphine is working for him, and that the night nurses will be respectful and kind. The bed is soft and warm too. Violet's asleep under a chair. My eyelids close tight against the night, missing Carlo and almost, but not quite, missing the rhythm of the rain which seems, for the time being, to have gone away.

Glossary of Terms

Allopathy – the dominant Western medical paradigm, based on the treatment of disease by its opposite (the prefix 'allo', from Greek, meaning 'other'), in contrast to homeopathy which is based on the law of similars (the prefix 'homo', from Greek, meaning 'like'). The recent trend to adopt the American spelling assists with pronounciation. It is now commonly spelt phonetically as 'homeopathy', though this makes it look more like something you do at home and may obscure the meaning for some.

CPD – Continuing Professional Development.

Dilution – the process by which material substances are made into homeopathic remedies. See Succussion.

EMF – Electromagnetic frequency.

Law of Similars – the basis of homeopathic prescribing. A substance that, in its material state, causes a symptom can cure the same symptom when administered in a homeopathic dose. Gave rise to the phrase 'like cures like.'

Maintaining Cause – a habit or situation that interferes with the process of cure.

Materia Medica – in homeopathy, this refers to books containing information about the remedies and the symptoms they treat. Information is collected from provings and clinical observation. Remedies are known by their Latin names.

Obstacle To Cure – this can be anything from an inherited susceptibility or weakness, to a habit which continually antidotes a remedy, to a mindset which needs to change. See Maintaining Cause.

Potentization – creating a remedy from a material substance by dilution and succussion, which renders it safe to take and does not produce side effects.

Proving – from the German, 'prufung', meaning 'test'. In order to know the action of a remedy, it is given in homeopathic doses to healthy human volunteers who do not know what they are taking. After repeated doses they produce various symptoms, which are then listed in the Repertory and Materia Medica.

Repertory – a dictionary of symptoms and the substances which have been shown to produce those symptoms, either in a material state, or in a homeopathic proving.

Rubric – an entry in the Repertory. Each rubric will have a list of remedies attached to it, graded according to the frequency with which they appeared in the proving.

RSI – Repetitive Strain Injury.

Succussion – a method of shaking the remedy in each stage of dilution, which activates its energetic properties. See Dilution.